English Taste
in the
Eighteenth Century
from
Baroque
to
Neo-Classic

Second Edition

Winter Exhibition, 1955-56

Royal Academy of Arts

London

PREFACE

It has been said that the arts of a period survive through the spirit of their inception. This is particularly true of the arts and crafts of the Eighteenth Century which once were the natural expression of their age and today are held in the greatest esteem. Various reasons have been assigned to the phenomenon of taste which accompanied the decorative arts during the reigns of the four Georges. The present exhibition is mainly concerned with the relationship between the fine arts and social culture, with the emphasis on the evolution of styles. The dominant theme in the period was an aristocratic one, but this admitted gradings in the interpretation of furniture and household appointments throughout society as a whole. For this reason alone the exhibition justifies itself not only for the lessons it conveys but because it accords with public interest in tradition and continuity. Since 1768 the Royal Academy has maintained the sequence of the fine arts in all their branches for it has long been recognised that the arts have an unity which is indivisible.

The organisers have provided one of the most eclectic displays possible from authentic sources. It is now generally agreed that England possesses historical examples which are both national and distinguished, ranking in quality with those of the leading continental countries. The broadest view of the art of the Eighteenth Century indicates three principal styles, the Baroque, the Rococo and a refined Neo-Classicism which is perhaps the most definite mark of assay. The centre of the great movement was London and from hence varied influences were carried to all parts of the kingdom as well as to the Continent and the American colonies. The elegancies of the time called forth the skill of the finest designers and craftsmen, capturing the imagination of the public and providing the middling people of those days with criteria of taste. A similar procedure is taking place today when everybody participates in a spirit of enquiry desirous of emulating the qualities of the national manner.

The objective of the winter exhibitions held under the auspices of the Royal Academy of Arts is to provide information which will inspire new spirit in all forms of art and social life. The present age is ready to be re-endowed with taste in which every member of the community can share. The inherent tendencies of the British people are opposed to dictation or art tyranny of any sort, hence the refusal to submit entirely to fashionable innovations which have little permanent value.

This exhibition should not only enable visitors to review the decorative designs of the phases of the particular period, but it should provide an index to subsequent developments. Never at any time in the long series of the Royal Academy's winter exhibitions has such a representative array of furniture, silver, porcelain and tapestries of the Eighteenth Century been shown. This is entirely due to the graciousness of Her Majesty The Queen and the generosity of all the other owners in allowing their treasures to be exhibited. The resulting display forms a brilliant parallel to the Exhibition of Portuguese Art in the adjoining rooms and affords the opportunity to study how certain phases of the arts of both countries were related.

It must not be forgotten that from 1714 down to the end of the century the English people lived amidst scenes of tranquillity which formed the background to everyday life. It was an age of quality and elegance in which artists and craftsmen pursued a common ideal. The merit of the period was the intrinsic value of its artistic contribution to the world at large. Small wonder then that the Eighteenth Century has impressed modern life so completely with its tenets of good sense. Curiously enough its mystic charm inheres in the direct statement and simplicity which epitomised English character at that time.

A just tribute is due to those who through their learning and labours have accomplished so successfully the task of selecting and arranging the exhibits. Under the chairmanship of Mr. John Wheatley, whose recent death on the 18th November is so lamented, Mr. Ralph Edwards, Mr. Brinsley Ford and Mr. Clifford Musgrave have given their time ungrudgingly; they have travelled hundreds of miles in their search for appropriate items and it is to their knowledge and enthusiasm that the high quality of the exhibition is due. I also acknowledge with gratitude the expert help of Mr. Charles Oman and Mr. George Wingfield Digby in the selection and cataloguing of the silver and the tapestries respectively.

The Committee have asked me to express their recognition of the valuable advice and suggestions from many other specialist authorities, among whom must be mentioned Mr. Edward Croft-Murray, Mr. Francis Watson, Mr. Donald King and Mr. Anthony Hobson.

The bulk of the catalogue has been ably compiled by Mr. St. John Gore in collaboration with the members of the Committee. It is largely due to Mr. Gore's industry that it has been possible to produce

PREFACE

so complete a publication in so short a time. The illuminating entries for the sculpture and the paintings have been contributed by Mr. Brinsley Ford.

A special feature of this catalogue is the Introduction by Mr. Ralph Edwards. This original and highly distinguished essay from the pen of the leading authority on English furniture and style is a notable addition to the literature of the subject. It will have a permanent value as such quite apart from its usefulness to all who visit the exhibition.

Finally I must emphasise that the organisation of this exhibition, and its opening within a few weeks of its companion from Portugal, has only been possible as a result of the labours of the Royal Academy's small but devoted staff.

A. E. RICHARDSON

COMMITTEE

* JOHN WHEATLEY, ESQ., A.R.A., *Chairman.*

RALPH EDWARDS, ESQ., C.B.E., F.S.A.

BRINSLEY FORD, ESQ.

CLIFFORD MUSGRAVE, ESQ.

Secretary: SIDNEY C. HUTCHISON, F.S.A.

* Died 18th November, 1955.

v

INTRODUCTION

By Ralph Edwards

The eighteenth century has strong claims to be regarded as the golden age of English taste. In the arts it was a period of restless creative energy when an extraordinary diversity of talents was fostered and encouraged by a cultured, cosmopolitan governing class. In the course of the century several distinct styles rose and waned, each in its turn being soon superseded to meet the demands of a capricious society ever intent on the latest mode.

This winter the Academy has devoted the galleries not occupied by Portuguese Art to another exhibition intended to illustrate, on a relatively small scale, the principal styles of the Georgian Era—Baroque, Rococo, Chinese, Gothic and Neo-Classic—fixing as a *terminus ad quem* the century's close, and thus omitting the last phase of neo-classicism, the archaeological revival popularly associated with the Regency. The Committee, avoiding so far as possible mixed or hybrid examples (for styles are often found blended, especially in the transitional phase), has given preference to those which show the various phases of taste in their quintessential or "most intense degree".

Throughout their long history decorative painting, the crafts and interior decoration have always been closely related to architecture, "the Mistress Art". This connection was particularly intimate in the Georgian period, and therefore the pictures, tapestries, furniture, silver, porcelain and other works of art here assembled inevitably lack the appropriate domestic environment for which many of them were purposely designed.

The exhibition is chiefly concerned with craftsmanship and the applied arts, for on painting, with the important exception of wall and ceiling decorations, the impact of the different styles was less direct; and, as in earlier times, it was mediated mainly through the influence of immigrant artists. To give a true picture of the cosmopolitan character of Georgian taste considerable additions would need to be made—Renaissance bronzes, for example, such as General Dormer collected to set on carved and gilt pedestals at Rousham (No. 88), blue-and-white and *famille verte* K'ang-hsi porcelain; and of course paintings by Claude, Salvator Rosa and Gaspar Poussin, to name only three masters whose works were highly regarded and eagerly acquired by English connoisseurs in the eighteenth century. It would moreover be apposite to show pictures of their foreign contemporaries whom they patronised, such as Vernet and Batoni, the painter of so many English travelling milords. But to do so would be to throw open the flood gates and to disregard the chronological limits: therefore the selection has been confined to works produced in this country within the given period (*circa* 1725–1800), and in a few instances, where it has seemed particularly relevant, to pictures painted by English artists abroad. Though nearly all the exhibits are thus of native origin, other exceptions are tapestries ordered from the Continent and Chinese wallpapers made for the European market, the import of such papers far exceeding the English imitations.

BAROQUE

Here we can only touch briefly on the complex history of these styles, but some explanation of the terminology is desirable. The current significance of Baroque in art history and criticism is far from precise, but it may be held to imply composition in mass, the substitution of a sense of dynamic movement for classic order, a thorough exploitation of plastic form and a bold, scenic use of light and shade: with these essential properties is mixed a considerable element of the grotesque. It has been said with some reason that "a cult of sensationalism" lies at the root of baroque art.

The term is associated in the first place with the architecture of the Counter-Reformation in Italy, and with all later architecture in which the same spirit prevails; but its use has been extended to painting and the minor arts. Thus it now covers a great variety of phenomena, ranging from the pictures of Caravaggio or Rubens and the sculpture of Bernini to furniture designed by the architect William Kent.

In England the first clear manifestations of the Baroque date from the Carolean age. Examples are to be found in Wren's designs for the rebuilding of Whitehall Palace; in late Stuart carved woodwork, furniture, textiles and silver; and also in the decorative field, notably in the painted ceilings of Verrio with their sprawling gods and goddesses in a degenerate Italianate idiom—a tradition long to be maintained.

A marked reaction towards simplicity of form and ornament under Queen Anne was followed by the second and more intensive phase of the style. Sir John Vanbrugh, architect and dramatist, was the supreme English exponent of the Baroque, and he had a worthy collaborator in Nicholas Hawksmoor (No. 77), whose contribution has not until lately received the recognition that it deserves. It is well to recall that Vanbrugh was engaged on his two most famous achievements, Castle Howard and Blenheim, throughout the Queen's reign; while Sir James Thornhill, the most gifted of our native decorative artists (some of his studies are shown in Galleries 11 and 10), began work on the ceiling of the Painted Hall at Greenwich so early as 1708. Thornhill's ample, vehement rhythms are in the true spirit of the Baroque, but while in architecture it scarcely outlasted the death of Vanbrugh (1726) in interior decoration and furnishing this grandiose, opulent style was first developed by architects for the ruling Whig oligarchy, and mainly confined to a few great houses built in accordance with the principles of Vitruvius and those of the Italian renaissance architect Andrea Palladio, as interpreted in England by the disciples of Inigo Jones.

Richard Boyle, third Earl of Burlington, "the Apollo of the Arts", both munificent patron and practising architect, had "a proper priest" in the person of William Kent, who after his return from a long stay in Italy (1719), having been introduced to the fashionable world by the Earl, soon won a great reputation by his versatility as an architect and designer (he was below mediocrity as a painter) and was treated as an oracle in matters of taste.

Of the surviving palatial Palladian houses, Holkham and Houghton in Norfolk are of exceptional interest for much of their contents was designed by Kent—the first English architect to bring movables within the scope of his decorative schemes. Through the generosity of their owners some representative examples are exhibited (Nos. 14, 82, etc.).

Kent's great sets of chairs and stools, pier glasses, pedestals and monumental side-tables, some in softwood, others in mahogany, painted or carved and gilt, are thoroughly baroque and Italianate in conception. He excelled at the free adaptation of Italian models, and his furniture, though apt to be overweighted with ornament ("immeasurably ponderous", so Horace Walpole declared), is perfectly congruous with the magnificent setting for which it was devised. Here we must forgo the bold, ornate plasterwork, often in full relief, of the Italian *stuccatori* employed by architects of Burlington's school and the rich figured Genoa velvets and damasks which, on the walls of saloons and reception-rooms, contributed so largely to the sumptuous effect.

Much of the costly furniture produced by fashionable cabinet-makers without the aid of architects, though unmistakably English, is yet fully consonant with the principles of the style. It was not confined to Palladian interiors nor to any one branch of the arts. For example, the terminal figures, gadrooning and other ornament employed on furniture and plasterwork also figure prominently on contemporary silver plate (No. 58).

In one of Hogarth's pictures, the well-known "Wanstead Assembly", now in America but shown lately at the Tate, Lord and Lady Castlemaine are seated amid lavish baroque splendours in the saloon at Wanstead, of which the ceiling was decorated by Kent—called by Hogarth "a contemptible dauber". But it is in the paintings of immigrant artists such as Sebastiano Ricci, Gianantonio Pellegrini and Jacopo Amigoni that some of the attributes of *seicento* Italian Baroque still linger—most notably in their ceiling decorations which, albeit at a far remove, continue the tradition (transmitted through Verrio and Laguerre) of Pietro da Cortona and other great mural painters of an earlier age.

The four panels by Amigoni from the hall at Moor Park (which have been restored and cleaned in time for this exhibition; Nos. 6, 15, 30 and 38) have been described by Professor Waterhouse as "very accomplished examples of Venetian Rococo"; but as their date (1732) anticipates the rise of Rococo in England, and they are the salient feature in a sumptuous baroque scheme of decoration, with which they are fully congruous, they are here associated with objects in that style.

ROCOCO

The Rococo (Galleries 9 and 8) is the anglicised version of the *rocaille*, "that phase of decorative art which, emerging in France about 1700 and characteristic of the reign of Louis XV, dominated Europe until the advent of classicism in the later years of the century". In contrast to the Baroque, from which it evolved, it is primarily a system of linear surface ornament, and in the land of its origin interior decoration was at first its principal sphere. Deriving its name from the *rocailleurs* who early in the seventeenth century devised elaborate grottoes for gardens, natural forms, rocks, foliage and flowers with animals, birds and human figures (freely stylised, and amusingly distorted) are all included in the wide decorative repertory. Abjuring plasticity and the straight line, the Rococo owes its distinctive character to the cult of assymetry—"C" scrolls and tortuous curves in an endless variety of intricate combinations.

We were comparatively slow to take the infection, and contracted it strongly just when the *rocaille* was being subjected to hostile criticism in France. Tell-tale motives appear in the ornament of English silver in the late thirties, and a few years later small pattern-books with engraved cartouches, sconces and shields were published by one of the chief pioneers of the movement, the carver and draughtsman, Mathias

Lock. In interior decoration, though a riot of scrolls and other rococo motives were introduced into plasterwork, we have nothing to rival the wonderful carved, gilt and painted rooms designed in Paris by leading decorative artists during the Regency and in the early years of Louis XV. But the Rococo triumphed over the whole range of domestic furniture with the publication in 1754 of the first edition of Chippendale's *Director*, where it is fully dominant, though combined with excursions into other contemporary styles.

Of the *rocaille* it has been truly observed that "imagination was the basis of it, and a combination of audacity and supreme technical skill was necessary for its development". The audacity and that "molten unity of form carried into every part with unparalleled verve and energy" which distinguishes the designs of J. A. Meissonier, the Turin decorative artist, were not nearly so conspicuous in England, but the technical ability was readily available. The spirit of the parent style was caught most successfully in the mirrors, sconces, stands, picture frames and console tables of soft wood, the work of specialist carvers and gilders. A medley of motives, asymmetrical in arrangement and often very disparate in character, are cleverly co-ordinated to produce a balanced design; and the best of such things possess a lively, fantastic charm and also a distinctive national character (Nos. 113, 131, 133).

In "case furniture"—commodes and cabinets—the failure to rival the daring curvature and subtle rhythms of the French prototypes is more noticeable, the designers' wilder imaginings remaining unrealisable aspirations, "sleighted", or retrenched, by craftsmen in the process of working them out. But the finest pieces, even when still reminiscent of the Baroque, have acquired a novel lightness and grace, giving point to Hogarth's contention in *The Analysis of Beauty* (1753) that all movables must needs be inelegant if their forms are not based on the principle of the curved line. In the craftsmanship extraordinary virtuosity is displayed; while, with a sure instinct for the proper function of ornament, delicate rococo carving is closely related to the structural lines of the design. Elaborate ormolu mounts of the kind favoured by famous *ébènistes* were rarely used and chiefly on "French commode tables". The bureau cabinet (No. 180), probably made by an immigrant craftsman, is highly exceptional, and here a "buhl" metal technique is also employed in the inlaid decoration.

If Chippendale may be regarded as the presiding genius of rococo furniture on the score of his famous book, as a maker he must now yield pride of place to William Vile, whose authenticated work is unrivalled by anything known to have been produced by Chippendale's

firm in that style. Vile (or someone in his workshop) was a designer
of marked individuality, given at times to rich exuberance of ornament
and with carvers and modellers of outstanding ability in his employ.

The pair of commodes from Goodwood (see No. 144) with their finely
modelled child-headed consoles are still Baroque in design, though they
date from about 1750, and in the ornament rococo details are introduced. Vile was employed to make furniture for George III and Queen
Charlotte soon after the King ascended the throne, and through Her
Majesty The Queen's gracious co-operation the exhibition includes
some of the superlative pieces obtained from him at that time. In the
"very handsome jewel cabinet" made for Queen Charlotte (No. 214)
and "the exceeding fine" secretary (to quote their maker's complacent
descriptions in the accounts) rococo decoration is combined with the
characteristic curvature of the style. On the other hand, the splendid
break-front bookcase of the Corinthian order (No. 196) is traditional,
even Palladian, in design while the carved ornament is predominantly
Rococo; though the secretary and bookcase date from 1761–62, when
the style was already on the wane.

Rococo, once established, proved highly contagious, and in the
decade 1750–60 spread over the whole decorative field, lingering on,
notably in silver and porcelain, some years after the general triumph
of other and hostile principles in the arts. The "true genius of porcelain", it has been claimed, is to charm and surprise, "and it was the
happiest accident that on its rediscovery in Europe its technique
should have come to maturity precisely in the period of the irrespons-
ible and capricious Rococo style. . . . It existed only for the delight
of a leisured class."

The quintessence of the rococo spirit is concentrated in this
medium, pre-eminently in Chelsea of the red and gold anchor periods,
expressing itself in the gay frivolity of the figures' poses, the curving
edges of table wares painted with naturalistic flowers in a delightful
dissonance of unnaturalistic hues; in the "Toys" with misspelt
French inscriptions, in which Cupid figures in many disguises, and also
in the tureens and dishes in the form of birds and animals; for "it
is one of the contradictions of Rococo that while indulging in a
riot of abstract scroll-work, it should have run also to naturalistic
forms. . . ."

If the impact of the style on painting was less direct, it was far from
negligible, and is clearly reflected through the influence of the immigrant artists in an increasing freedom of design, a distinct infusion of
alien grace, and a more sensuous appreciation of the qualities of the
medium.

Despite Hogarth's violent insular prejudices, his borrowings from French painters and engravers amount in the aggregate to quite a considerable debt. Though formal values are by no means ignored, *The Analysis*, with its constant emphasis on Intricacy and Variety, the waving and serpentine lines of Beauty and Grace, is an essay upon a theme essentially Rococo. "The Dance" (seen last winter at the Academy) is probably the source of Plate 2 in *The Analysis*, and a convincing demonstration of Hogarth's theory that flickering, "serpentlike" form expresses motion. It is significant that the design should be indebted to one of Coypel's illustrations, but there are already distinct rococo tendencies in the sketches for a Royal portrait group or conversation (No. 106) dating before Hogarth began to concentrate on his "painted stage".

Henri Gravelot, a draughtsman and engraver rather than a painter (and for that reason not represented here), may be singled out from these artists of foreign origin as "the prime sponsor of the Rococo and French manner, which did much to break down Augustan formality and reached its purest English flowering in the early work of Gainsborough". And in the master's later pictures with their intricate rhythms, light, fluent brushwork and feathery foliage the rococo spirit persists long after the eclipse of the style in the decorative arts (e.g. No. 110).

Philippe Mercier, son of a Huguenot refugee, was for a while in the service of Frederick, Prince of Wales, as "principal painter". Dismissed by the Prince, he retired into Yorkshire, where he stayed for some years and enjoyed a good practice in portraits and "conversations". Rococo characteristics, with a mild Teutonic admixture, are to be found in a number of Mercier's paintings (No. 136). On his first visit to Rome (1736–38) Allan Ramsay studied at the French Academy, and in the 1750's his portraiture reflects the influence of La Tour and Nattier. This pervasive influence may be held partly responsible for his captivating elegance. In Lord Ilchester's "Caroline, Lady Holland" (No. 97) there are charming rococo accessories, but here the design has an almost classic repose and there is none of the flutter of draperies and lively sense of movement we associate with contemporary portraiture in France.

In sculpture it is to Roubiliac, the Huguenot refugee, rather than to the Flemings, Rysbrack and Scheemakers or any native competitor, that we must look for the nervous tension, vivacity and animation (more apparent in his terra-cotta models than in his marble busts), that contrasts so forcibly with the "high Roman manner" and heroic classical conventions of English sculpture in the Baroque age. The judgement of his contemporary, George Vertue, that in his models and busts "his invention (is) very copious and free picturesque; light and easy as painting", is a naive attempt to summarise the rococo qualities with which they are so strongly imbued.

CHINOISERIE

The Chinese and Gothic styles, or "tastes" as they were called (Gallery 7 and the Architectural Room), are commonly thought of as tributaries of the Rococo, but both were flowing strongly long before they poured into the main flood. The vogue for Chinoiseries represents the latest and most intense expression of an old enthusiasm, a curiosity long since awakened in the art of a remote and mysterious land.

From the first years of the seventeenth century lacquered screens and porcelain had been brought home by ships of the East India Company, and this traffic vastly increased after the Restoration when prodigious quantities of lacquered furniture, textiles and curiosities were imported; while the imitation of lacquer by "japanning", the western process, attained the dimensions of a fashionable craze. During the early Georgian period the taste, though never extinct, declined; but towards the middle of the century there was a widespread revival of interest, and architects, designers and ornamentalists once again turned their attention to the Far East. To some extent the demand was fostered by books of travel, of which the principal was Du Halde's great work on China, translated into English in 1741; but, paradoxically, the style derived much of its distinctive character from the prevalent deep ignorance and misconceptions about the art and culture of the Orient. The promoters of the movement relied largely on their own bizarre, romantic fancies, supplemented by the vague impressions which they derived from imported wares—mainly from screens and decorative porcelain made in huge quantities to satisfy the avid European demand. Thus the taste was for *Chinoiserie*, a transposition, or extremely free rendering into western terms of some of the more superficial aspects of Oriental art. As such it caught on and by 1749 "the barbarous gaudy *gout* of the Chinese" could be already denounced by a champion of symmetry and classical order. A visitor, arriving in London, might fancy himself in the Empire of China, and—a few years later—"according to the present prevailing whim everything is Chinese or in the Chinese taste . . . chairs, tables, chimney-pieces, frames for looking-glasses, and even our most vulgar utensils are all reduced to this newfangled standard", and that, too, omits the frivolous ventures in the open air—bridges, "triumphal arches" and temples.

INTRODUCTION

In pattern-books, the *Director* and others, the vogue was freely exploited and many absurdly grotesque designs were produced, though few of the more bizarre fancies were ever realised. For the most part, the distinctive motives—the "pagoda" or pseudo-Oriental upward curving roof, employed as a cresting, latticework, and the ubiquitous characteristic frets, stylised Chinamen and ornithologically impossible long-necked birds—were skilfully blended with the existing rococo repertory of ornament and often employed with captivating effect; in the more extreme instances reaching a crescendo of delightful whimsicality. Despite its detractors' complaints, the style obtained only a limited vogue. In a large house a bedroom, and perhaps a boudoir, would be devoted to it where, as formerly at Badminton and still at Claydon, it would be found in a highly concentrated form—the walls "covered with Chinese paper filled with figures which resemble nothing in God's creation"; the bed with painted oriental silk; the chimney-piece with gilded dragons writhing over it and mounting to the inevitable pagoda; the furniture largely of imported lacquer or English japanning; and the whole fantastic assembly designed in that distinctive version of the style which a writer in *The World* (1753) was fully justified in proudly claiming to be no mere copy but "of our own invention".

The founder of this "Sharawadgi taste" in England (in France and Germany it had a long tradition and a contemporary vogue) was, according to Walpole, his friend Richard Bateman, who later deserted it for the Gothic "so effectively that every pagoda took the veil". In 1756 it was said by Isaac Ware to be "now left to coffee-houses and Sunday apprentices"; but this was premature, for Sir William Chambers, the only architect with personal knowledge of the Far East, supplied one or two specimens of authentic furniture in his *Designs for Chinese Buildings* (1757), though he was at pains to disclaim any extravagant admiration of Oriental art. By 1765 the craze was declining, but towards the end of the century it enjoyed an Indian summer of popularity, when a lavishly equipped Chinese drawing-room was fitted up for the Prince of Wales at Carlton House. The unique pair of side-tables decorated in polychrome (No. 255), still in the Royal Collection, were formerly among the contents of this once celebrated room. Designed by Henry Holland, they witness to the versatility of that gifted architect, whose name is chiefly associated with a style that made no concessions to such engaging frivolity.

At the height of the vogue Anglo-Chinese motives infiltrated into the decoration of porcelain (as they had done into that of English Delft long since) and on Worcester of the middle years of the century,

Chinese figures, birds and landscapes are rendered with an airy delicacy and grace. Some of the earliest figure sculpture in porcelain was of Chinamen, and in Chelsea and early Derby there are a number of models with chinoiserie subjects after Boucher and from Meissen models or engravings. In contemporary plate there was none of the characteristic engraved ornament employed in late Stuart times and Chinoiserie was confined to tea-pots, caddies and epergnes. Painting was almost untouched by the vogue. Reynolds's portrait of Wang-y-tong (No. 258) dates after the decline, and is only indirect evidence of the lively curiosity that the rare Chinese visitor to England continued to excite. We have nothing to compare with the enchanting chinoiserie drawings of Jean Pillement.

GOTHIC

The inception of the "Gothic taste", as it was known to the admirers and inventors of mock medieval forms in architecture, furniture and decoration, preceded that of the Chinese by nearly a decade. "An attempt of the romantic spirit to blossom in an arid and unpropitious soil", as such it was a forerunner of the Romantic Movement, while it looked backward nostalgically to a misconceived and freely roman ticised past. The so-called "Gothic Revival" of the mid-century is inseparably associated with Horace Walpole's name; and with some justification, since his zeal and social standing did much to propagate it. He took up the vogue when it was no longer the *dernier cri*, and in the architectural domain his celebrated experiment, Strawberry Hill— the transformation of "a small tenement" was spread over many years—does not entitle him to rank as a pioneer. Only in a relatively brief interval after the Reformation was there no gothic building in England, and in spite of the apparent triumph of classic principles, the interest in medieval art had been strongly stimulated and re-awakened before the advent of Walpole and his school. As the contemporary Chinoiserie owed much of its distinctive character to ignorance, so again, paradoxically, it was William Kent, the high priest of Palladianism, who "evolved the flimsy decorative equivalent for Gothic which was to persist throughout the eighteenth century"— and far beyond. Sham medieval ornament was grafted on to a classic foundation in an audacious attempt to gratify the whim of a group of dilettanti by bringing the art of the Middle Ages up to date. Walpole derided the experiments of Kent and other dabblers in the resuscitated style, and favoured a closer reliance on medieval forms. In the interior of Strawberry Hill (which still retains some of its original embellishments) the chief decorative features devised by Walpole and his friends who formed the "Committee of Taste" were transcripts or ingenious adaptations of medieval architecture and monuments—a ceiling pilfered from fan vaulting in stone, the carved ornament of a chimney-piece from a famous tomb. Thus the venerable style was travestied to meet modern requirements (and herein lay both the novelty and the weakness) in a blend of rococo fantasy and eclectic antiquarianism. No consistency was attempted in the furnishing. The owner had a vast miscellaneous collection of various periods and styles, and as he also set store by "modern comfort", the activities of the "Committee" were not much in evidence. But they were represented, and a pair of gothic mirrors in the Refectory (see No. 299) were, according to the *Description of Strawberry Hill* (1774), "designed by Mr. Walpole", and are therefore exceptional as he very rarely took pencil in hand.

In *The Director* and the publications of Chippendale's rivals, save for one or two ventures in the "pure" style, the characteristic detail is used merely as a piquant flavouring. A "Gothic Sideboard" will have the supports pierced with cusped arches and rococo ornament elsewhere; a cabinet or a chamber-organ will be crowned with a forest of finials; the arcading of a chair-back will shamelessly consort with cabriole legs. But by the more austere devotees a closer adherence to their principles was demanded, and wherever the structure allowed, as on chairs, rococo detail was banished, arcading, crockets and finials being assembled to form a complete stylistic unity. Mid-Georgian Gothic was always the cult of a coterie, and furniture designed in the "true taste" as distinct from hybrid specimens is rare. Henry Keene "Surveyor of the Fabric of Westminster Abbey" and Sanderson Miller, the Warwickshire squire, who had contrived Gothic ruins for himself and his friends, gothicised Tudor Arbury for Roger Newdigate in a thoroughgoing manner inside and out; but the owner's zeal seems almost to have spent itself before he came to the furnishing. Apart from the book-cases fitted into the walls of the library, Newdigate apparently contented himself with a set of gothic chairs and a settee (see No. 267). Similarly, John Chute, who was one of the members of the "Committee", at the Vyne indulged his Walpoleian predilections very sparingly, though he introduced scenic painted decorations of an unprecedented kind (No. 291), into the finest real gothic private chapel in England.

The taste was described (in *The World*) as outmoded and deserted by fashion for the Chinese early in the fifties, but this was to dismiss it a good deal too soon: the influence of Strawberry—a well-known showplace—contributed to give it a new lease of life. The plates of gothic furniture were still retained in the third edition (1762) of *The Director*, and "the most approved patterns" for chairs in the taste were offered to the public in 1766.

In architecture the Gothic of Walpole, improved upon later by James Wyatt, was to linger on until discredited by Pugin and other Victorian purists. Lee Priory by Wyatt, which Walpole hailed as "a true child of Strawberry", finished "by a great master", and so far superior to its parent, was not completed until 1785. A melancholy interest attaches to salvage from that lately obliterated and memorable house (Nos. 289 and 292), where mock-medieval was carried to the zenith by the exquisite quality of the interior detail. Gothic gained no adherents among designers of silver and porcelain, and on the Continent there was no parallel cult.

NEO-CLASSIC

The Neo-Classic style (Lecture Room) which, when it had gathered momentum, was to oust the Rococo and dominate architecture and the allied arts throughout the second half of the eighteenth century was the outcome, as the term implies, of a reawakened interest in the remains of the ancient world, primarily in those of Greece and Rome. An enthusiasm for the arts of classical antiquity (in architecture mainly through the medium of Renaissance interpretations) had of course manifested itself long before, but towards the mid-century it received a powerful stimulus from the recent discoveries at Herculaneum and Pompeii (*Le Antichita di Ercolano*, an "epochal work" in a magnificent form, appeared at intervals from 1755 onwards); and in the same decade there was a series of other publications by scholarly travellers of various nationalities. Of these, Robert Wood's *Ruins of Palmyra* (1753), followed four years later by another treatise on those of Baalbec (which an admirer hoped might "expel the littleness of the Chinese and the barbarity of the Goths"), with Stuart and Revett's *Antiquities of Athens* (1762), were among the earliest and most important for the extent of their influence on English taste.

But in England Robert Adam was the protagonist and leading exponent of the classical revival both in architecture and the decorative field. After three years in Italy, varied by excursions to Sicily and Dalmatia, where he surveyed the ruins of Diocletian's palace at Spalato (an enterprise commemorated by a sumptuous book), he returned to London in 1758, began to practise, and with his earliest commissions generated, to quote Sir John Soane, "the electric power of that revolution in art"—so potent a force that within a brief time "everything was Adamitic, buildings and furniture of every description". In 1761 Adam produced his plans for the remodelling of the interior of Syon, which the Duke of Northumberland decreed should be "entirely in the antique style", and this undertaking where, as he observes, "the opportunity was great and the expense unlimited" may be taken to mark the spectacular rising of his star. Here we are not concerned with Adam's architecture, and with his interior decoration only on account of its intimate relation to the movables: where he was at liberty to realise his ideals these were all made to conform closely to their environment. Adam claimed to be responsible for a complete revolution in the character of interior decoration and furniture; and, if taken to refer to the homes of a few great magnates, the claim can scarcely be denied. And, incidentally, the inauguration of this far-reaching change considerably antedates the parallel development in France.

For "the massive entablature, the ponderous compartment ceiling" and kindred plasterwork enrichments of the Palladian school Adam substituted "a beautiful variety of light mouldings gracefully formed and delicately enriched", aiming to capture, not so much the letter, as "the beautiful spirit of Antiquity, and translate it with novelty and variety". This new decorative convention was based on the remains of Greek and Roman buildings and on the arabesques or *grotteschi* adapted by Raphael in the Vatican loggia and the Villa Madama from classic originals—a species of ornament at which William Kent had already tried his hand. The stucco decoration in relief, on a ground of pale blue, green, rose-pink and other pastel-like shades, was at first relatively large in scale, but gradually dwindled to a rather finicky delicacy. In "houses of consequence" decorative painting was brought into close stylistic harmony with the plaster enrichments. As earlier in the century, most of the leading practitioners were Italians—Zucchi, Cipriani, Biagio Rebecca and Angelica Kauffmann are perhaps the best known—and they filled the inset panels of ceilings and walls with subjects from classical mythology over-sweet and cloying in sentiment, but in colour and tone admirably calculated to enhance the decorative effect. Architects of the older generation adopted the new style and imitated Adam in an endeavour to compete with him; though the movement had its opponents, like Sir William Chambers, who stigmatised its enrichments as "filigrane toy-work", contrasting it unfavourably with the more virile Palladian mode of his youth.

Adam perfected the process of integrating movables with their environment which William Kent had begun. In the state rooms of the great houses for which he was responsible he sought to establish a complete synthesis: everything, furniture, carpets and fittings, bore the impress of a single directing mind and was brought within the compass of an all-inclusive style. So close was his attention to the smallest details that, as Soane puts it, he gave "an elegance and importance even to the key-hole of a lady's escritoire".

In furniture designed by Adam and his followers the same motives occur as in mural plaster enrichments—the anthemion, or honeysuckle ornament, for borders; paterae, medallions and festoons of husks. Torchères, tripods and pedestals adapted from classic prototypes were largely employed in saloons and drawing-rooms to support vases and candelabra. The furniture for such apartments was of ceremonial character intended to minister to "the parade of life". A characteristic innovation is the sideboard flanked by pedestals supporting urns, which now took the place of the isolated side-table. A set of this kind, faultless alike in proportion and craftsmanship, was designed by Adam for the Eating Room of 20 St. James's Square, and on the removal of modern paint and gilding the original colour matching the decoration of the walls was revealed (Nos. 384 and 386).

Though in the third edition of *The Director* (1762) there is no trace of classic influence, within a few years Chippendale, working in some instances under Adam's direction, had thoroughly assimilated the new ideals; and to a few great houses he supplied marquetry furniture inlaid with a variety of exotic woods in the neo-classic style—the group at Harewood is deservedly the most famous (No. 334)— which is of extraordinary distinction and fully comparable with the masterpieces of contemporary French *ébènistes*.

Pervasive as was his influence, the degree of Adam's responsibility as an exponent of neo-classicism should not be exaggerated. Other architects and designers of movables achieved distinctive interpretations of the style: it soon became widely diffused and some of the furniture by William Gates, John Cobb or John Linnell will bear comparison with the productions of Chippendale's firm (e.g. Nos. 360 and 361). Adam's designs were laid under contribution and adapted by cabinet-makers for a wider clientèle, and in the *Works in Architecture* (the first volume was published in 1773) one of the plates is stated to illustrate "pieces of furniture which were first invented for particular persons but are since brought into general use". In trade pattern-books of the last quarter of the century, such as those of Hepplewhite and Sheraton, the style is almost emptied of its classic content and, "in order to combine the useful with the agreeable", skilfully rendered into vernacular terms. Painted and inlaid decorations became smaller in scale, pretty and naturalistic in character.

INTRODUCTION

The influence of neo-classicism on easel painting was far-reaching but partial and intermittent in its more intensive form: it never achieved a comprehensive victory, and throughout the last half of the century pictures continued to be painted in a plurality of styles. The artists most affected were those long resident in or paying long visits to Rome, where they came into contact with Raphael Mengs, the leading executant of the classical school, and Johann Winckelmann, whose publications mark an epoch in the study and appreciation of ancient art. Gavin Hamilton, painter, excavator and dealer, and Benjamin West, future President of the Academy, in the early sixties absorbed the principles of classicism at the fountain head, and were the first English practitioners in this style. Hamilton concentrated on subjects from the *Iliad*, doubtless in deference to Winckelmann's insistence on the superiority of all things Greek: his "Hector's Farewell to Andromache" (1772), an enormous picture still extant, "is almost a Jacques Louis David *avant la lettre*". West at the outset did the same kind of thing "Poussin size" and his "Final Departure of Regulus from Rome" (1769) was the first of many commissions for George III, who patronised the "American Raphael" on an excessively generous scale. It is difficult for us to understand the admiration which such early neo-classical performances evoked. These groups with strained rhetorical gestures look as if they have been painstakingly put together from bas-reliefs, and are now mainly of interest as important documents in the history of taste (Nos. 383, 385 and 395).

The "Grand Style" as conceived by Reynolds in the *Discourses*, and to some extent in his own practice with its eclecticism and "hints accumulated from the best masters", did not imply a rigid adherence to the classical code as understood by its first and more fanatical exponents. The subject, if possible, should be one "in which men are universally concerned" and "the great events of Greek and Roman fable", if not strictly universal, would suffice. In the Augustan tradition the wearing of classical draperies was *de rigueur*, but Reynolds condemned anything precisely indicative of time or place. The historical painter, if he would not "debase his conception", must avoid minute discrimination, concentrating on the disposition of the folds; while he who sought "to dignify his subject" must not paint a lady in contemporary costume which, being so familiar, would defeat his end, but give her robes "something of the general air of the antique for the sake of dignity and preserve something of the modern for the sake of likeness".

This was to "generalise" in the President's sense, and many full

length portraits of the seventies prove that he observed the rules he
had laid down. Peeresses and leaders of fashion in draperies of a
vaguely classical caste, such as certainly were never worn, masquerade
as heroines or goddesses, perhaps with some distinguishing symbol of
rank, sacrificing at flaming altars or posed beside a classical term or
vase (No. 396). Other portrait painters emulated Sir Joshua, and
ladies in the role of Hebe or Thais would be provided with mythological attributes, sometimes with an oddly incongruous effect (No.
378).

The main achievements of the neo-classic school were on a scale
which precludes their adequate representation. James Barry, whose
vast canvases at the Society of Arts (painted between 1777 and 1783)
are his most impressive memorial, was among the few English aspirants
to the Grand Style in "history painting", and one of his earliest
exhibits at the Academy was derisively described as "executed upon
the large elevated plan of the Greek statuaries and poets". Most of
his works, despite his undeniable gifts, have long been consigned to
oblivion; while the majority of history painters showed no conviction
or consistency in their concessions to classical ideals, rendering
scriptural and medieval as readily as antique themes. West, though a
protagonist of the revival, scored his greatest popular success with
"The Death of Wolfe" (1771), in which, contrary to all precedents, the
General and his companions were depicted in modern uniforms.

Neo-classic sculpture of the last half of the eighteenth century is a
subject far too wide and important to allow of more than a brief
reference here. Moreover, no just estimate of it can be formed from
the marble busts of celebrities which, as in earlier times, were in great
demand; rather it must be judged by its many sepulchral monuments and statues. Like contemporary painters, English sculptors,
such as Banks and Flaxman, who studied in Rome came under the
influence of Winckelmann's disciples, and on their return disseminated
his theories, particularly his cardinal tenet of the superiority of the
Greeks. From it was deduced "the fatal doctrine" of the Ideal
and Typical, which spread over Europe and was based on the belief
that the Greeks sought to generalise, deliberately avoiding the specific
and individual, a notion largely inspired by inferior copies which
Winckelmann and his disciples supposed to be originals.

Large numbers of statues, busts, bas-reliefs, cinerary urns and other
antiquities were supplied to English collectors by compatriots who had
settled in Italy. Of these agents Gavin Hamilton, the artist, as
excavator and dealer was most conspicuously successful, and from
him Charles Towneley (who had himself made a long stay in Italy)

obtained many of the principal ornaments of his celebrated collection. Zoffany's well-known picture "Mr. Towneley in his Gallery of Statues" (No. 406) is highly evocative of this particular enthusiasm, confined to a small circle of wealthy connoisseurs. It represents the owner's library at 7 Park Street, Westminster, though, as Nollekens's biographer J. T. Smith observes, "not strictly correct as to its contents, since all the best of the marbles displayed in various parts of the house were brought into the painting by the artist, who made it up into a picturesque composition according to his own taste". The hall and chief reception rooms were crammed with the statues shown in the picture and many more, the whole collection being acquired for the British Museum soon after Towneley died in 1805.

But elsewhere a gallery was set apart or specially constructed to contain antique marbles, as at Newby Hall, Yorkshire, where the Sculpture Gallery remains today exactly as the owner, William Weddell (No. 352), and Robert Adam arranged it about 1775, and "is the best example in this country of the beau-ideal of a classical cogniscente : the meticulous reconstruction of a Roman interior according to the evidence of Herculaneum and the Catacombs". No survey, however summary, of English Taste in the eighteenth century should omit any reference to such galleries, now nearly all long since dispersed. Of contemporary sculptors Joseph Nollekens, who was quite unaffected by the Grecian rage, had the largest clientèle among leaders of society for portrait busts—dull and uninspired as many of them may seem to us—and he added considerably to his ample professional income by buying and "botching up" antique statues, ingeniously supplying missing members, not always without intent to deceive.

English pottery and porcelain of this period were subjected to classic influence in varying degrees, but it was by Josiah Wedgwood, who won an international reputation, that this style was most consistently and thoroughly exploited. His cream-coloured, black basalt and jasper wares, materials obtained as the result of long experiment, were eminently well adapted for the realisation of his aim, which was to make the whole of his vast output conform to the fashionable classical ideal. Thus, for all their "pure" forms and irreproachable taste, his productions are almost wholly derivative— a host of Italians in Rome supplied him with classic reliefs for adaptation—and with their minute mechanical perfection of finish, alien to the technique and tradition of English craftsmanship. The rather chilly finger of neo-classicism was also laid on the chief English porcelain factories—first and most firmly by William Duesbury at Derby from soon after 1770 onwards; but even so, lightly; and there, as also at Worcester, rococo models and fashions were revived some years after the general eclipse of that style.

Derby figures in the "cold and literal" biscuit, a material imitated from Sèvres, are the fullest expression of neo-classicism and in porcelain foreshadow the end of a great age.

In silver the style achieved a universal victory, though into the early seventies rococo detail lingers on. As in the case of Wedgwood's wares, antique amphorae, urns and vases supplied the models for modern objects of similar kind, while for those, the great majority, for which no ancient prototypes existed, forms more or less congruous with classic precedent were cleverly devised. The ornament, applied in the finer pieces with an instinctive feeling for its appropriate relation to the design, is a microcosm of the motives employed in contemporary furniture and decoration.

In the last gallery of the exhibition visitors cannot fail to admire the general high level of craftsmanship, which is particularly notable at this period, and the admirable resource displayed in the adaptation of ancient forms to new purposes; but they may well be conscious of a distinct drop in the *tempo*. The vigorous creative impulse has died down, lively fantasy and endless fertility of invention are superseded by rule and precedent. Classic order and discipline inevitably exact a price.

GENERAL INFORMATION

THE Exhibition opened on Saturday, December 3, 1955, and closes on Sunday, February 26, 1956.

Hours of Admission: Week-days, 10 a.m. to 7 p.m.
Sundays, 2 p.m. to 6 p.m.

Price of Admission, 2s. Season Ticket, 10s.

Catalogue, 1s. 6d. (by post 1s. 9d.).

Illustrated Souvenir, 3s. 6d. (by post 4s.).

Visitors are required to give up their sticks and umbrellas before entering the Galleries; they must be left with the attendants at the Cloak Room in the Entrance Hall. The other attendants are strictly forbidden to take charge of anything.

Invalids may obtain the use of a wheeled chair during certain hours, without charge, by previous arrangement with the Secretary, to whom application should be made for the necessary order.

PLAN OF THE GALLERIES

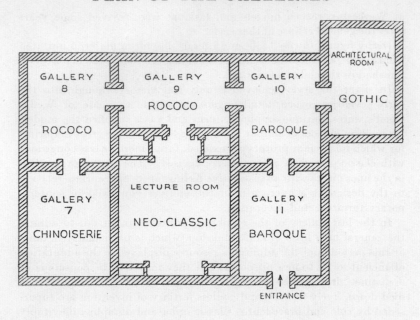

EXPLANATORY NOTES

In the measurements the height is given first followed by the width and, where applicable, the depth.

B.F.A.C. = Burlington Fine Arts Club.

D.E.F. (*1927*) = The Dictionary of English Furniture by Ralph Edwards and Percy MacQuoid (3 vols., 1924–27).

D.E.F. = The Dictionary of English Furniture, revised by Ralph Edwards (3 vols., 1954).

MacQuoid, Age of . . . = A History of English Furniture by Percy MacQuoid (4 vols., *Oak, Walnut, Mahogany, Satinwood,* 1904–8).

R.A. = Royal Academy Summer Exhibition.

R.A. Winter = Royal Academy Winter Exhibition.

CATALOGUE

GALLERY XI

BAROQUE

1 Pair of Carved and Gilt Brackets

H. 24 in., *c.* 1740. Supports of scroll form, carved with foliage, terminating below shelf in volutes.
Lent by Mrs. Lindsay-Fynn.

2 Carved and Gilt Mahogany Armchair

35½ × 30 × 23 in. Designed by William Kent, *c.* 1730. From a set. Arms terminate in lions' heads; lion masks on knees, apron centring in satyr mask. Covered in contemporary green velvet. En suite with No. 5. Lit: MacQuoid, *Age of Mahogany*, p. 42, fig. 36: p. 46.
Lent by the Marquess of Cholmondeley.

3 Carved, Painted and Parcel-gilt Console Table

33½ × 60 × 28 in., *c.* 1730. Composition marble top decorated with arabesques and arms of Walpole; acanthus scrolls of apron centring in mask; key pattern frieze, scroll legs. Coll: possibly the gift of Horace Walpole to his friend John Chute. Lit: A. Tipping, "Furniture at The Vyne," II, *Country Life*, Vol. XLIX, 1921, p. 649.
Lent by Sir Charles Chute, Bt.

WILLIAM HOGARTH (1697–1764)

4 The Wollaston Family

Canvas. 30 × 49 in. Signed and dated: *Wm. Hogarth: Fecit: 1730.* Exh: Arts Council, London, *William Hogarth*, 1951, No. 17. Lit: R. B. Beckett, *Hogarth*, London 1949, p. 47, Pl. 31. Painted in 1730, this picture shows an interior typical of the 1720's. The engaged fluted Corinthian columns, the scallop shells over the doors and the architectural type of chimney-piece surmounted by a bust are recurrent features in the interiors associated with the Palladian style. The tea-table is Kentian, verging on Rococo, silvered and of a type which is not extant. William Wollaston (1693–1764) of Finborough Hall,

Suffolk, is with his wife, Elizabeth Fauquier and a number of their relations. The scene is probably the Wollaston town house in St. James's Square. (See Beckett, *op. cit.*, for details of sitters.)
Lent by Capt. H. G. Wollaston.

5 **Carved and Gilt Mahogany Chair**

$39 \times 23 \times 23$ in. Designed by William Kent, *c.* 1730. From a set of twelve. Lion masks on knees, apron centring in satyr mask; covered in contemporary green velvet. En suite with No. 2. Lit: MacQuoid, *Age of Mahogany*, p. 42, fig. 37: p. 46.
Lent by the Marquess of Cholmondeley.

JACOPO AMIGONI (1675–1752)

6 **Jupiter and Io**

Canvas (shaped top). 141×121 in. Lit: F. J. B. Watson, *English Villas and Venetian Decorators*, R.I.B.A. Journal, Vol. 61, Ser. 3. No. 5 (March 1954); C. Hussey, *English Country Houses: Early Georgian*, London 1955, p. 43.

Styles, a city magnate who had made a large fortune at the time of the South Sea Bubble, purchased the XVIIth Century house of Moor Park in 1720, and employed Leoni to reconstruct it. For the decoration of the interior with paintings in the baroque style he at first employed Thornhill, but, having quarrelled with him, dismissed him, and, as a deliberate affront to the English artist, engaged the Venetian painter Amigoni, recently arrived from abroad, to replace Thornhill's decorations in the hall at Moor Park with four large canvases of scenes from the legend of Jupiter and Io. At Moor Park the walls above these canvases are painted in *chiaroscuro* with figures in niches. These are probably the remains of Thornhill's earlier decorations. The Amigoni paintings were completed by 1732, when Vertue saw them (*Vertue, III, 63*). Amigoni, assisted by Sletter, another Venetian artist, did a considerable amount of decoration in other parts of Moor Park.

Amigoni was the last of the great Venetian decorative painters to come to this country. He arrived towards the end of 1729 and remained here until 1739 (except for a short visit to Paris in 1736), when he returned to Venice and is said to have been instrumental in persuading Canaletto to come to London. At the time Amigoni arrived here the taste for decorative painting in the style favoured on the Continent, never very deeply rooted in England, was passing. Although he at first enjoyed some success as a decorator, he was soon driven to adopt the more profitable line of portrait painting in which he obtained the patronage of the royal family and the nobility. (The above note has kindly been supplied by Mr. Francis Watson.)

The question as to whether Amigoni should properly be labelled a baroque or rococo artist is one on which critics may agree to differ. But, as discussed in the Introduction, the date of these paintings anticipates the rise of Rococo in England, and as, at Moor Park, they are the salient features in a sumptuous baroque scheme of decoration, with which they are fully congruous, they are here associated with objects in that style.

The story of Io (from the *Metamorphoses* of Ovid, Book I) recounts how Jupiter became enamoured of the nymph Io and, to protect her from the jealousy of Juno, changed her into a heifer. Juno, suspicious of trickery, asked for the heifer and handed her over to the keeping of the hundred-eyed Argus. Jupiter ordered Mercury to slay Argus. This he did after first lulling Argus to sleep. Juno then took the eyes of Argus and placed them on the feathers of her peacock, "covering its tail with jewelled stars". After endless wanderings Io was restored to human shape and gave birth to Epaphus.

The four paintings by Amigoni were greatly obscured by dirt and discoloured varnish. They have recently been cleaned at the expense of the Rickmansworth Urban District Council, and they are now seen for the first time in many years in all the beauty of their original colouring.
Lent by Rickmansworth Urban District Council.

7 **Carved and Parcel-gilt Walnut Chair**

$42 \times 24 \times 27$ in., *c.* 1715–20. Square legs, hipped on seat-rail, ending in hoof feet; covered in contemporary green velvet. En suite with Nos. 8 and 9. Lit: *D.E.F.*, I, p. 260, fig. 105.
Lent by the Marquess of Cholmondeley.

8 **Carved and Parcel-gilt Walnut Settee**

$42 \times 79 \times 31$ in., *c.* 1715–20. Six square legs ending in hoof feet; covered in contemporary green velvet. En suite with Nos. 7 and 9. Building operations began at Houghton in 1721; the set of which this settee is part may well have come from the earlier house. There is a gilt chair in the Victoria and Albert Museum, with legs and feet of the same pattern, made for Sir William Humphreys, Lord Mayor of London, which can be dated about 1717. The settee and

two chairs are shown in order that all the principal sets of seat furniture at Houghton, made for Sir Robert Walpole, should be represented. Lit: *D.E.F.* (1927), III, p. 91, fig. 21.
Lent by the Marquess of Cholmondeley.

9 Carved and Parcel-gilt Walnut Winged Armchair

46 × 35 × 31 in., *c.* 1715–20. Square legs, hipped on seat-rail, ending in hoof feet; covered in contemporary green velvet. En suite with Nos. 7 and 8.
Lent by the Marquess of Cholmondeley.

10 Pair of Carved and Gilt Sconces

34½ × 21½ in. Attributed to Benjamin Goodison, *c.* 1730. Foliage finials on cresting flanked by satyr masks with pendants of oak leaves and acorns; bases with lion masks holding wreaths of bay leaves, shell motifs above; candle-branches missing. Lit: Leeds Arts Calendar, Vol. 6, No. 21, p. 6.
Lent by Leeds Art Gallery (Temple Newsam House).

ANDREA SOLDI (b. 1703–*c.* 1771)
11 William Hogarth

Canvas. 67 × 45 in. The identity of the sitter has been questioned. Soldi came to England in about 1736 where he would presumably have known his contemporary, Hogarth (1697–1764). To begin with, Soldi met with success, as is proved by the fact that between April and August, 1738, he painted no less than thirty portraits. By 1744 his extravagances had landed him in a debtors' prison. His friends got him out and he recovered much of his practice, but he died penniless and was only saved from a pauper's grave by the charitable fund of the Royal Academy. (See W. T. Whitley, *Artists and their Friends in England*, 1700–99, 1928, Vol. I, pp. 51, 121–3.)
Lent by Capt. V. M. Wombwell.

12 Carved and Gilt Side-table

35 × 55 × 27 in. Attributed to Benjamin Goodison, *c.* 1730. Siena marble top; scroll legs with fish-scale and acanthus decoration; apron of acanthus and floral festoons centring in stylised shell. Lit: *D.E.F.*, III, p. 286, fig. 40.
Lent by the Leeds Art Gallery (Temple Newsam House).

13 Wine Cistern

H. 27 in.   By David Willaume, 1728.   Tower-shaped; decorated with strapwork; two handles and tap.
Lent by the Duke of Rutland.

14 Carved and Gilt Armchair

48 × 29 × 28 in.   Designed by William Kent, *c.* 1730.   From a set of twelve; hooped back, baluster arms with scale decoration, "broken" cabriole legs with Indian masks; upholstered in contemporary cream and crimson Italian velvet. Lit: *D.E.F.*, I, p. 267, fig. 130: p. 271.
Lent by the Marquess of Cholmondeley.

JACOPO AMIGONI (1675–1752)

15 Argus lulled to Sleep by the Flute of Mercury

Canvas (shaped top).   141 × 132 in.   See No. 6.
Lent by Rickmansworth Urban District Council.

16 Carved and Gilt Side-table

34½ × 53 × 27 in.   Probably by William Bradshaw, *c.* 1730.   Marble top supported on scroll legs; apron centring in lion's mask. Lit: R. Edwards and M. Jourdain, *Georgian Cabinet Makers*, London 1946, fig. 49.
Lent by the Earl Stanhope.

17 Carved and Gilt Armchair

42 × 28 × 27 in.   By James Miller, *c.* 1760.   From a set in an earlier style; curved arms carved with acanthus, scaling and "money-moulding"; cabriole legs, finishing in volutes, similarly decorated. Contemporary Italian velvet supplied by the firm of Benjamin Goodison.   James Miller, a carver, worked at Holkham after 1760 (see C. W. James, *Chief Justice Coke*, 1929, p. 280). Lit: *D.E.F.*, I, p. 269, fig. 135; p. 271.   *Cf.* No. 89.
Lent by the Earl of Leicester.

18 Carved and Gilt Chair

39 × 24 × 23 in., *c.* 1730.   Scroll legs, seat-rail decorated with key-pattern, flower garland below; top formed of double cornucopiae; covered in contemporary silk damask.   *Cf.* No. 49.
Lent by the Earl of Leicester.

GALLERY XI

JOHN ALEXANDER (Active 1710–1757)

19 Pluto and Proserpine: Sketch for a Ceiling

Canvas. $28 \times 31\frac{3}{4}$ in. Signed and dated: *J Alex^r in^t & pinx^t. A.D. 1720. (JA* in monogram). Lit: *Catalogue, National Gallery of Scotland*, 1946, p. 65; E. K. Waterhouse, *Painting in Britain, 1530–1790*, London 1953, p. 240, Pl. 166 (b). Probably the modello for the enormous canvas (which no longer survives) for the roof of the staircase at Gordon Castle. Professor Waterhouse describes the large canvas as "the unique example of Scottish baroque painting".
Lent by the National Gallery of Scotland.

20 Pair of Mirrors in Carved and Gilt Frames

$72 \times 41\frac{1}{2}$ in. Designed by William Kent, probably for the 3rd Earl of Burlington, Chiswick House, *c.* 1730. Carved with scroll-work, pendants of husks, paterae, swags of acorns and other baroque motifs; on the cresting, owls with outspread wings.
Lent by the Trustees of the Chatsworth Settlement.

21 Carved and Gilt Side-table

$33\frac{1}{4} \times 54\frac{1}{2} \times 26\frac{1}{4}$ in. Designed by William Kent, probably for the 3rd Earl of Burlington, Chiswick House, *c.* 1730. Eagle terminals; in their beaks swags of fruit, forming apron with pendant in centre; top inlaid with agates and various stones on black marble ground. Lit: *D.E.F.*, III, p. 285, fig. 34: p. 288.
Lent by the Trustees of the Chatsworth Settlement.

22 Silver Tray

$17\frac{1}{4} \times 13\frac{1}{2}$ in. By Eliza Godfrey, 1744. Edge with masks and festoons; arms and inscription in centre. Presented to Christ Church by the 2nd Duke of Buccleuch.
Lent by Christ Church, Oxford.

23 Pair of Carved and Gilt Oak Armchairs

$37\frac{1}{2} \times 24 \times 21$ in. Designed by William Kent for the 3rd Earl of Burlington, Chiswick House, *c.* 1730. Underframe of X-form, arms lion-headed, cresting carved with acanthus scrolls; covered in silk damask of later date. Lit: *D.E.F.*, I, p. 269, fig. 133; p. 271.
Lent by the Trustees of the Chatsworth Settlement.

BAROQUE

SIR JAMES THORNHILL (1675–1734)
24 **Scene from the Life of St. Paul: St. Paul preaching at Athens**
Canvas. 32¼ × 29 in. See No. 25.
Lent by the Dean and Chapter of St. Paul's Cathedral.

SIR JAMES THORNHILL (1675–1734)
25 **Scene from the Life of St. Paul: St. Paul preaching before Sergius Paulus**
Canvas. 32¼ × 29 in. Coll: presented by the N.A.C.F. to St. Paul's Cathedral, 1953. Lit: N.A.C.F. *Fiftieth Annual Report 1953*, repr. facing p. 23. This sketch and No. 24 are of subjects from the Apostle's life and were probably early designs for two segments of the dome of St. Paul's Cathedral; they are also, in a sense, alternative designs in respect of the architectural surround. The sketches were no doubt made by Thornhill when he thought that the work would be carried out in colour; they are characteristic examples of his preliminary oil sketches for a large mural decoration, and contain several elements taken from the Raphael Cartoons which Thornhill greatly admired (quoted from N.A.C.F. Report). For the history of Thornhill's decoration of the dome, see No. 47.
Lent by the Dean and Chapter of St. Paul's Cathedral.

26 Carved and Gilt Side-table
31½ × 59½ × 31 in. Designed by William Kent, probably for the 3rd Earl of Burlington, Chiswick House, c. 1730. Scroll terminals, apron of acanthus leaves centring in female mask; black marble top. Lit: M. Jourdain, *The Work of William Kent*, London 1948, p. 173, fig. 137.
Lent by the Trustees of the Chatsworth Settlement.

27 Silver-gilt Basin and Ewer
H. (Ewer) 23 in. Diam. (Basin) 20 in. By Benjamin Pyne, 1721. Exh: Goldsmiths' Hall, *Historic Plate of the City of London*, 1951, No. 214. Goldsmiths' Hall, *Corporation Plate of England and Wales*, 1952, No. 114. Helmet-shaped ewer with open scroll handle; round basin, with coat of arms.
Lent by the Corporation of London.

SIR GODFREY KNELLER (1646 or 1649–1723)
28 **Lady Elizabeth Cromwell and her Sisters**
Canvas. 24 × 29 in.
Lent by the Executors of the late Miss Hilda Mary Inge.

29 **Carved and Gilt Oak Chair**

$36\frac{3}{4} \times 25\frac{1}{4} \times 20$ in. Designed by William Kent for the 3rd Earl of Burlington, Chiswick House, c. 1730. Scroll legs, female masks on knees, cresting of acanthus scrolls centring in shell; covered in silk damask of later date. Lit: *D.E.F.*, I, p. 269, fig. 133: p. 271.
Lent by the Trustees of the Chatsworth Settlement.

JACOPO AMIGONI (1675–1752)

30 **Mercury about to slay Argus**

Canvas (shaped top). 141×132 in. See No. 6.
Lent by Rickmansworth Urban District Council.

31 **Pair of Carved and Gilt Console Tables**

$33 \times 40 \times 22$ in., c. 1730. Marble tops supported on fabulous monsters with lions' bodies finishing in dolphins' tails. (Formerly at Ingestre Hall, Staffs.) No close counterparts to these tables have been recorded.
Lent by the Marquess of Anglesey.

32 **Carved and Gilt Mahogany Armchair**

$40 \times 34 \times 26$ in., c. 1730. Lion-headed arms and lion legs, with paw feet; covered in contemporary English needlework. Lit: *D.E.F.*, I, p. 266, fig. 127: p. 271.
Lent by the Duke of Norfolk.

33 **Pair of Carved and Gilt Pedestals**

H. 56 in. By Benjamin Goodison, 1732–33. In the form of terms, headed by female busts bearing Ionic capitals; scroll feet. Lit: *D.E.F.*, III, p. 159, fig. 1.
Lent by Her Majesty The Queen (Hampton Court).

34 **Pair of Silver-gilt Wall Sconces**

$30\frac{1}{2} \times 22$ in. No marks. About 1735 (the branches by John Bridge, 1830). Probably made for Frederick, Prince of Wales. Decorated with classical figures, masks and crown and cipher. Exh: Victoria and Albert Museum, *Exhibition of Royal Plate*, 1954, No. 37.
Lent by Her Majesty The Queen (Buckingham Palace).

35   Mirror in Carved and Gilt Frame

65 × 40 in., *c.* 1730. "Broken" pediment; cresting with feathered female mask; consoles with pendant oak leaves at sides.
Lent by the National Trust (Stourhead).

36   Carved and Gilt Side-table

36 × 56 × 28 in., *c.* 1730. Verde Antico marble top supported on scroll legs headed by satyr masks; eagle bracket in centre. Lit: *D.E.F.*, III, p. 288–9, fig. 43.
Lent by the Earl of Shaftesbury.

MICHAEL RYSBRACK (1694–1770)

37   1st Duke of Marlborough

Marble bust. H. 36 in. Lit: M. I. Webb, *Michael Rysbrack, Sculptor*, London 1954, p. 95. John Churchill, 1st Duke of Marlborough (1650–1722), diplomat and general, victor of the War of the Spanish Succession. The present bust is regarded by Webb as probably coming from the workshop of Rysbrack, the original being the one presented by the Duchess of Marlborough to the Bodleian in 1730, now in the Ashmolean Museum. Other versions at Blenheim, Wimborne St. Giles and in the National Portrait Gallery.
Lent by the Duke of Northumberland.

JACOPO AMIGONI (1675–1752)

38   Juno receiving the Head of Argus from Mercury

Canvas (shaped top). 141 × 121 in. See No. 6.
Lent by Rickmansworth Urban District Council.

39   Carved and Gilt Mahogany Armchair

40½ × 36 × 25 in., *c.* 1725. Eagle motifs on legs and arms, claw-and-ball feet; contemporary needlework introducing eagles' heads. Lit: *D.E.F.*, I, p. 266, fig. 125: p. 268.
Lent by the Duke of Norfolk.

40   Silver Tea-kettle and Stand

H. 40 in. Stand by David Willaume, 1717. Kettle (maker's mark illegible), 1724, octagonal with domed cover and swing handle; stand with baluster stem and tripod base.
Lent by the Duke of Buccleuch.

41 Mirror in Carved and Gilt Frame

43 × 27 in. By Benjamin Goodison: one of three made for Frederick, Prince of Wales, 1732–33. Cresting centring in Prince of Wales's feathers; with two brass candle branches. Lit: *D.E.F.*, III, p. 333, fig. 57: p. 334.
Lent by Her Majesty The Queen (Hampton Court).

WILLIAM KENT (?1684–1748)
42 Architectural Landscape with the Return of the Prodigal Son

Canvas. 41½ × 35½ in. Coll: painted for the 3rd Earl of Burlington. In 1719 Kent returned from Italy to England as a protégé of Lord Burlington, who recommended him as a painter of portraits and historical subjects. In 1721, through the influence of Burlington, he received a commission from the King for the redecoration of Kensington Palace where he worked until 1725 painting a number of ceilings and the staircase. As a painter Kent was also employed by Sir Robert Walpole at Houghton between 1728 and 1730, by Lord Townshend at Raynham in about 1730, and at Hampton Court from 1732–35 where he painted the Queen's great staircase and the guard chamber (see Trenchard Cox, "William Kent as Painter," *Artwork*, 1931, VII, 25). This painting appears to be an essay by Kent in the manner of Sebastiano Ricci. Kent was employed at Burlington House, where he would have been familiar with the three large canvases and the ceiling painted by Ricci.
Lent by the Trustees of the Chatsworth Settlement.

43 Painted and Gilt Sideboard Table

33½ × 67½ × 35 in. Attributed to Mathias Lock, *c.* 1735. Marble top, supported by coupled consoles; apron carved with mask of Hercules and lion trophies. Coll: Ditchley House. Lit: *D.E.F.*, III, pp. 123–4, fig. 3.
Lent by the Leeds Art Gallery (Temple Newsam House).

44 Silver Winecooler

13 × 23½ × 19½ in. (Weight 555 oz.) By Francis Nelme, 1731. Oval with handles in the form of griffin and unicorn; lower part of body decorated with strapwork and medallions.
Lent by the Duke of Buccleuch.

BAROQUE

GAWEN HAMILTON (1698-1737)

45 The Earl of Strafford and his Family

Canvas. 36 × 32 in. Lit: Ralph Edwards, *Early Conversation Pictures*, London, 1954, p. 170. Thomas Wentworth, 1st Earl of Strafford (of the 2nd creation), 1672-1739. In his youth he fought in Flanders under Marlborough. For some years he was Ambassador at Berlin. He was in secret communication with the Old Pretender by whom he was created Duke of Strafford in 1754. He is seen with his wife Anne, daughter and heiress of Sir Henry Johnson of Bradenham, his son William (b. 1722), and his three daughters Anne, Lucy, and Henrietta. The setting in which the Earl is depicted with his family is a typical Palladian interior. The room itself has not been identified but Mr. Edwards points out that it does not correspond with the hall in the Palladian mansion, Wentworth Castle, which the Earl built for himself near Barnsley, Yorkshire. The Earl also had a house at Twickenham. Vertue (III, 61) writing in 1732 says that Gawen Hamilton painted "A family piece of the present Earl of Strafford himself, his Lady, his Son and daughters in the Conversation way" for which he was paid ten guineas. Edwards reproduces (Pl. 91) another almost identical version, signed and dated 1732, which belongs to Mrs. Daniel Carstairs, Philadelphia.

Lent by the Lady Elizabeth Byng.

46 Carved and Gilt Walnut Armchair

38 × 31 × 22 in., *c.* 1725. From a set of twelve. Arms terminate in eagles' heads, apron pendant, cabriole legs with honeysuckle ornament and claw-and-ball feet; upholstered in French green damask. Lit: *D.E.F.*, I, p. 266, fig. 126; pp. 268, 271.

Lent by the Marquess of Cholmondeley.

GALLERY X

BAROQUE

SIR JAMES THORNHILL (1675–1734)

47 Scene from the Life of St. Paul: The Conversion of St. Paul

Canvas. 30 × 20 in. After the completion of St. Paul's Cathedral, about 1709–10, it was decided to decorate the interior of the dome with paintings. A number of foreign artists came to London in the hope of securing the commission. These included the French painters Pierre Berchet and Louis Cheron and the Venetians Pellegrini and Sebastiano Ricci. Eventually the commission was given to Thornhill, who, according to Vertue (II, 125), ousted Laguerre, who had first been chosen by the Commission. Vertue (I, 162) says the work was begun in September 1715 and completed within four years by September 1719. This set of eight finished monochrome oil sketches depicting scenes from the life of St. Paul corresponds with the subjects in the dome. The set was probably prepared for the engravers after the paintings in the dome had been completed. A number of Thornhill's drawings for the dome are in the British Museum while Nos. 24 and 25 in this exhibition are probably earlier oil sketches prepared when Thornhill thought that the work would be carried out in colour. Thornhill is the greatest baroque painter this country has produced. *Lent by the Dean and Chapter of St. Paul's Cathedral.*

SIR JAMES THORNHILL (1675–1734)

48 Scene from the Life of St. Paul: St. Paul preaching before Sergius Paulus

Canvas. 30 × 20 in. See No. 47.
Lent by the Dean and Chapter of St. Paul's Cathedral.

49 Pair of Carved and Gilt Chairs

$38\frac{1}{2}$ × $22\frac{1}{2}$ × 18 in., c. 1730. Scroll legs, seat-rail decorated with key pattern, flower garland below; top formed of double cornucopiae; silk cover of later date. These chairs, in painted pinewood, correspond with No. 18. Lit: P. MacQuoid, *English Furniture . . . in the Lady Lever Art Gallery*, London 1928, No. 100, Pl. 29.
Lent by the Lady Lever Art Gallery.

50 Mahogany Cabinet

102 × 59 × 34½ in., *c.* 1745. Pediment carved with naval trophy; pendant rococo ornament and nautical instruments; lower stage fitted with twelve drawers with gilt-brass handles. Lit: Oliver Brackett, *English Furniture Illustrated*, revised by H. Clifford Smith, London 1950, Pl. CXXVIII.

Lent by the Ministry of Works (The Admiralty).

SIR JAMES THORNHILL (1675–1734)

51 Scene from the Life of St. Paul: The Sacrifice at Lystra

Canvas. 30 × 20 in. See No. 47.

Lent by the Dean and Chapter of St. Paul's Cathedral.

SIR JAMES THORNHILL (1675–1734)

52 Scene from the Life of St. Paul: Conversion of the Gaoler at Philippi

Canvas. 30 × 20 in. See No. 47.

Lent by the Dean and Chapter of St. Paul's Cathedral.

BARTHOLOMEW DANDRIDGE (1691–working *c.* 1754)

53 William Kent

Canvas. 35 × 27 in. Coll: purchased 1909. Lit: M. Jourdain, *The Work of William Kent*, 1948, pp. 43–4, repr. frontispiece; H. M. Colvin, *Dictionary of English Architects*, pp. 341–6. William Kent (?1684–1748) first came into prominence as the protégé of Lord Burlington. His versatility was prodigious. In architecture he was not only responsible for Palladian buildings of the importance of Holkham Hall and the Horse Guards but he designed a villa at Esher which anticipates by twenty years the Gothic of the 1750's. He designed stuccos, frames, chimney-pieces, sculpture, bridges, obelisks, temples, triumphal arches, gateways, monuments, stage scenery, plate, candelabra, and the state barge made for Frederick, Prince of Wales, which is now in the Victoria and Albert Museum. He illustrated books and he is even said to have invented a lady's dress decorated with columns of the Five Orders, so that she seemed "a walking Palladio in petticoats". In landscape gardening Kent "leaped the wall", as Walpole puts it, "and saw that all Nature was a garden". In this exhibition it has only been possible to illustrate two aspects of his genius. As a painter, in which case the word genius is hardly applicable, he is represented by No. 42. As a

designer of furniture he is represented by some of his most famous work. This includes chairs, carved and gilt pedestals, side-tables, looking-glasses, and a mahogany writing-table made for his patron the 3rd Earl of Burlington; from Houghton there are specimens from all the magnificent suites, and from Holkham some fine examples of the furniture he designed for that house.
Lent by the National Portrait Gallery.

54 Tapestry: Echo and Narcissus

Silk and wool on woollen warp. 108 × 170 in. Woven in Antwerp for the English market, c. 1700. Signed: *M.W.* See No. 87.
Lent by the Duke of Buccleuch.

55 Carved and Gilt Console Table

30 × 36 × 20 in., *c.* 1730. One of a pair; top, carved in low relief, supported by sphinxes resting on plinth; the gilding has been renewed. Lit: MacQuoid, *Age of Mahogany*, p. 17, fig. 15.
Lent by the Duke of Beaufort.

56 Pair of Carved and Gilt Pedestals

H. 51¾ in. Designed by William Kent and probably made by Benjamin Goodison for the 3rd Earl of Burlington, Chiswick House, *c.* 1730. In the form of terms headed by busts of children bearing Ionic capitals festooned with leaves. Lit: *D.E.F.*, III, p. 159, fig. 2.
Lent by the Trustees of the Chatsworth Settlement.

57 Carved and Gilt Side-table

34 × 78 × 36 in., *c.* 1730. Top veneered with Siena marble; scrolled supports carved with lion motifs, united in front by apron of fruit and flowers, centring in escutcheon with lion's mask; Vitruvian scroll frieze.
Lent by the Earl of Onslow.

58 Silver Winecooler

19¼ × 40 × 21 in. By Gabriel Sleath, 1720. Coll: Sir Ambrose Crowley; Ashburnham Sale (Christie's, 25th March, 1914); presented to the Grocers' Company by the Directors of the Bank of England, 1917. Exh: Goldsmiths' Hall, *Historic Plate of the City of London*, 1951, No. 211. Oval with harp-shaped handles, side with acanthus and gadrooned ornament; interior of bowl with arms of Crowley impaling Gascoigne.
Lent by the Worshipful Company of Grocers.

59   Carved and Gilt Console Table

$32 \times 26 \times 26$ in., *c.* 1730.   One of a pair; top, carved in low relief, supported by eagle; the gilding has been renewed.   Lit: MacQuoid, *Age of Mahogany*, p. 16, fig. 14.
Lent by the Duke of Beaufort.

60   I Quattro Libri dell'Architettura di Andrea Palladio (Venetia, Dominico de' Franceschi, 1570)

First Edition, small folio, 4 books in one, bound in early XVIIIth-Century diced Russian gilt, with gilt dentelle borders and centre ornaments in the Harleian style.   Formerly the property of Richard Boyle, 3rd Earl of Burlington (1695–1753), with his autograph signature on the dedication-leaf followed by the date, *Feb. 1, 1727/8.*
Lent by Francis Stonor, Esq.

GEORGE KNAPTON (1698–1778)

61   3rd Earl of Burlington

Canvas. 49×40 in.   Signed and dated (on back of canvas, under relining): *George Knapton, pinx. 1743.*   Lit: F. Saxl and R. Witt-kower, *British Art and the Mediterranean*, 1948, Nos. 53–60 "The Dictatorship of Taste," repr. 53 (1).   Richard Boyle, 3rd Earl of Burlington and 4th Earl of Cork (1695–1753), was responsible for reintroducing the Palladian taste into England in the early XVIIIth Century.   In this painting, as Professor Wittkower writes: "Lord Burlington is holding his own edition of Palladio's drawings and in the background stands the bust of Inigo Jones.   It is not by chance that Jones's ghostlike look is fixed on the living trustee of his architectural work.   Burlington wanted to appear before his friends and contemporaries as 'Il Palladio e il Jones de' nostri tempi', to quote from a dedication to him by the Italian antiquarian Scipione Maffei."   Lord Burlington's presence in the baroque section may appear somewhat equivocal since the movement he championed aimed at the restoration of classical rule and order, as a reaction against the baroque tendencies of Wren and Vanbrugh.   But it is as the patron of Kent and of Sebastiano Ricci that Lord Burlington has a rightful place in this exhibition, for to quote Professor Wittkower again: "Many large rooms from Inigo Jones's day onwards until about the middle of the eighteenth century were profusely decorated and more in line with the grandeur of international Baroque than with the classical severity of their own exteriors.   In a note in his Roman sketch-book of 1614 Inigo Jones has given the reason for this contrast between inside and outside.   'All the composed ornaments which

39

proceed out of the abundance of designers and were brought in by Michelangelo and his followers, in my opinion do not well in solid architecture and the façade of houses, but in gardens, loggias, stucco or ornaments of chimney-pieces or in the inner parts of houses those compositions are of necessity to be used. For as outwardly every wise man carries a gravity in public places, where there is nothing else looked for, yet inwardly has his imagination set on fire, and sometimes licenciously flying out, as nature herself does oftentimes stravagantly. . . .'"

Lent by the Trustees of the Chatsworth Settlement.

62 Walnut Settee

38 × 51 × 23 in., *c.* 1740. Arms terminate in lions' heads; at front cabriole legs with paw feet; covered in contemporary needlework.
Lent by Mrs. David Gubbay.

MICHAEL RYSBRACK (1694–1770)

63 Inigo Jones

Marble bust. H. 18½ in. Coll: executed for the 3rd Earl of Burlington, for his villa at Chiswick, prior to 1743 since it appears in Knapton's portrait (see No. 61). Lit: M. I. Webb, *Michael Rysbrack, Sculptor*, London 1954, pp. 80, 102, Pl. 37. Inigo Jones (1573–1652). Amongst his best-known buildings are the Queen's House at Greenwich and the Banqueting Hall in Whitehall. In spite of his relatively small architectural output his importance in the history of English art can scarcely be overrated for he revolutionised the standard of taste and was himself the first English artist to acquire a continental reputation. (See M. Whinney, *Chambers's Encyclopædia*, 1950, VIII.) Lord Burlington has acknowledged his admiration for Inigo Jones by having this bust introduced into the background of his own portrait by Knapton. Aubrey (*Brief Lives*, edited by A. Clark, 1898, Vol. II, p. 10) states that the bust on Inigo Jones's tomb was rescued at the time of the great fire in 1666, and he made a sketch of the whole monument in which it appears. This bust is no longer extant but very possibly was in Rysbrack's time, and it seems likely that he would have founded his own work on it rather than on a picture or print.
Lent by the Trustees of the Chatsworth Settlement.

64 Pair of Carved and Gilt Brackets

H. 13 in., *c.* 1735–40. Shelves supported on eagles with outspread wings; pomegranate pendants.
Lent by Mrs. David Gubbay.

BAROQUE

JACOPO AMIGONI (1675–1752)

65 Frederick, Prince of Wales

Canvas. 50 × 40 in. Coll: bt. by George IV (as an "unknown nobleman"): Carlton House Inventory 1816, No. 319. Frederick, Prince of Wales (1707–51), eldest son of George II. His estrangement with his father led to his becoming the centre of an opposition, in which he was associated with Bubb Dodington, Bolingbroke and others. Vertue in 1735 (III, p. 75) refers to the Prince "at length in Garter Robes" by Amigoni. A full-length portrait is now at Raby Castle.
Lent by Her Majesty The Queen (Buckingham Palace).

66 Mahogany Card-table

30¼ × 42 × 40¾ in., c. 1740. Frieze carved with festoons of vine leaves centring in front with Bacchic mask; legs with paw feet; on shoulders lion masks with rings.
Lent by the National Trust (Stourhead).

67 Parcel-gilt Mahogany Balloting Box

16 × 16 × 12½ in. Made for the Society of Dilettanti, 1737–38. Designed by George Knapton and executed by Thomas Adye. Pedimental top, figure of Justice astride cylinder; decorated with masks, medallions and reliefs. Lit: G. A. MacMillan, *The Society of Dilettanti*, London 1932, pp. 26–30, Pl. IVA.
Lent by the Society of Dilettanti.

MICHAEL RYSBRACK (1694–1770)

68 George I

Marble bust. H. 26½ in. Signed: *M. Rysb^k Fec^t·* Coll: presented to the College by Dean David Gregory (d. 1767). Lit: Mrs. Poole, *Catalogue of Oxford Portraits*, Oxford 1925, Vol. III, p. 50, No. 127; M. I. Webb, *Michael Rysbrack, Sculptor*, London 1954, pp. 179, 216. Included in Vertue's MS. list of Rysbrack's works (III, p. 56) with the note that the King did not actually sit for it.
Lent by Christ Church, Oxford.

69 Mahogany Armchair

39½ × 35 × 26 in., c. 1730. Arms finishing in lions' heads; lions' masks on all four legs; tapestry cover of later date. Lit: *D.E.F.*, I, p. 265, fig. 122; p. 268.
Lent by the Earl of Leicester.

GALLERY X

70 Mahogany Commode

37 × 41 × 22 in. Attributed to William Vile, *c.* 1740. One of a pair; three drawers, marble top; lion-headed consoles; frieze carved with key-pattern and paterae; enrichments gilt. Coll: H.M. Queen Mary, Marlborough House. Lit: *D.E.F.*, II, p. 111: fig. 3, p. 109.
Lent by Her Majesty The Queen (Buckingham Palace).

71 Pair of Oval Mirrors in Carved and Gilt Frames

102 × 60 in. Probably by Samuel Norman, *c.* 1750–60. Frames carved with fish-tailed winged female figures, with scroll-work and garlands of fruit below; crestings formed of lyres between acanthus foliage. Between 1759–60, Samuel Norman, a fashionable cabinet-maker in partnership with James Whittle and John Mayhew in King Street, Covent Garden, supplied a number of splendid carved and gilt mirrors to Woburn and this pair may well have been among them. They possess vestigial baroque characteristics suitable to the architect Henry Flitcroft's interior. See G. Scott Thomson, *Family Background*, London 1949, pp. 63–78, *passim*.
Lent by the Duke of Bedford.

72 Pair of Parcel-gilt Mahogany Pedestals

H. 65 in. Attributed to Benjamin Goodison, *c.* 1740; probably supplied by him to the 1st Lord Folkestone for the Gallery at Longford, finished in 1739–40. Tapered shafts headed by busts of Hercules. Lit: *D.E.F.*, III, p. 159, fig. 4.
Lent by the Earl of Radnor.

73 Needlework Carpet

140 × 108 in., *c.* 1740–50. Embroidered in wool and silk in tent stitch on linen canvas; the design of strapwork, flowers and foliage scrolls.
Lent by Mrs. David Gubbay.

74 Parcel-gilt Mahogany Armchair

40½ × 30 × 27 in. Attributed to Giles Grendey, *c.* 1739; one of a set obtained for Longford by the 1st Lord Folkestone. Covered in contemporary green Italian velvet over which pierced guilloche moulding is applied. Padded arms terminate in lions' heads; acanthus foliage decoration. Lit: *D.E.F.*, I, p. 265, fig. 123: p. 268.
Lent by the Earl of Radnor.

75 Mahogany Winecooler

21½ × 40 × 27 in., *c.* 1730. Carved with gadroons, mounted with four gilt-metal lions' heads with rings. Lit: *D.E.F.*, III, p. 372, fig. 2: p. 374.
Lent by the Earl Spencer.

76 Mahogany Library Writing-table

35¼ × 57 × 30¼ in. Designed by William Kent for the 3rd Earl of Burlington, Chiswick House, *c.* 1730. Designed to stand against a wall; carved and gilt enrichments, owl-head terminals and claw-and-ball feet. Lit: *D.E.F.*, III, p. 244, Pl. IX: p. 249.
Lent by the Trustees of the Chatsworth Settlement.

SIR HENRY CHEERE (1703–1781)

77 Nicholas Hawksmoor

Plaster bust. H. 24 in. Lit: Mrs. Poole, *Catalogue of Oxford Portraits*, Oxford 1925, Vol. II, p. 189, No. 32, Pl. XXV. Nicholas Hawksmoor (1661–1736) was associated with Wren from an early age. Later he became Clerk of the Works at Kensington Palace (1689), Greenwich Hospital (1698), and Whitehall, Westminster and St. James's (1715); he assisted Vanbrugh at Castle Howard and Blenheim and became his deputy as Comptroller of the Works. As such he collaborated with his master in the baroque style. As an architect in his own right he was responsible for works with gothic (additions to All Souls, Oxford, and Westminster Abbey) and Roman (Mausoleum, Castle Howard) elements. (See H. M. Colvin, *Dictionary of English Architecture*, 1954, pp. 272–7.)
Lent by All Souls College, Oxford.

78 Tapestry: Arcas Shooting at the Bear

Silk and wool on woollen warp. 108 × 92 in. Woven in Antwerp for the English market, *c.* 1700. See No. 87.
Lent by the Duke of Buccleuch.

79 Mahogany Library Writing-table

31½ × 57 × 30 in. Designed by William Kent for the 3rd Earl of Burlington, Chiswick House, *c.* 1735. Applied ornaments of gilt-brass and wood repeated on both sides; convex ends. Lit: *D.E.F.*, III, p. 245, fig. 13: p. 249.
Lent by the Trustees of the Chatsworth Settlement.

MICHAEL RYSBRACK (1694–1770)

80 George II

Marble bust. H. 24¾ in. Lit: Mrs. Poole, *Catalogue of Oxford Portraits*, Oxford 1925, Vol. III, p. 65, No. 168; M. I. Webb, *Michael Rysbrack, Sculptor*, London 1954, pp. 156, 179, 216. The bust is similar to the signed marble at Windsor made for Queen Caroline's New Library in St. James's Park for which the terracotta model, signed and dated *1738*, also exists at Windsor. Vertue (III, pp. 84, 85) mentions that the King's bust was modelled from life.
Lent by Christ Church, Oxford.

JONATHAN RICHARDSON (1665–1745)

81 Sir John Vanbrugh

Canvas. 42 × 34 in. Coll: purchased by the College of Arms, 1824. Sir John Vanbrugh (1664–1726), soldier, playwright and the greatest English exponent of baroque architecture; Comptroller of H.M. Works 1702–13, and again in 1715 on the return to power of the Whigs; succeeded Wren as surveyor to Greenwich Hospital. He was created Clarenceux King of Arms in 1704. His greatest architectural commissions were Castle Howard (1699–1726) and Blenheim Palace (1705–1720). The best-known portrait of Vanbrugh is the kit-cat by Kneller, painted when he was about forty, and now in the National Portrait Gallery.
Lent by the College of Arms.

82 Carved and Parcel-gilt Mahogany Settee

49 × 48 × 24 in. Designed by William Kent, *c.* 1730. One of a pair. High cresting with acanthus decoration on scaled ground, scroll legs with female masks, deep apron of acanthus scrolls centring in large shell. Covered in contemporary Italian crimson velvet. En suite with No. 83. Lit: *D.E.F.*, III, p. 87, fig. 39: pp. 92, 98.
Lent by the Marquess of Cholmondeley.

83 Carved and Parcel-gilt Mahogany Stool

21 × 24 × 22 in. Designed by William Kent, *c.* 1730. From a set of six. Scroll legs with female masks, shell pendant festooned with oak leaves. Covered in contemporary Italian crimson velvet. En suite with No. 82. Lit: MacQuoid, *Age of Mahogany*, pp. 71–3, fig. 66
Lent by the Marquess of Cholmondeley.

BAROQUE

MICHAEL RYSBRACK (1694–1770)

84 Andrea Palladio

Marble bust. H. 19½ in. Coll: executed for the 3rd Earl of Burlington for his villa at Chiswick. Lit: M. I. Webb, *Michael Rysbrack, Sculptor*, London 1954, p. 80, Pl. 36; p. 102. The head of Andrea Palladio (1518–1580) was taken from an engraved portrait in the possession of Lord Burlington. Dated by Webb (*op. cit.*) *c.* 1725.
Lent by the Trustees of the Chatsworth Settlement.

FRANS VAN DER MIJN (1719–1783)

85 Sir Thomas Robinson

Canvas. 49 × 39½ in. Signed and dated: *F. Van der Mijn 175(?).*
Coll: probably Sir Thomas Robinson, Bt.; Sir William Robinson, Bt., 1777, 1st Lord Rokeby, 1785, and thence by inheritance to the Hon. Elizabeth Robinson Montagu. Sir Thomas Robinson, 1st Bt. (*c.* 1700–77), celebrated as a man of fashion, also achieved some distinction as an amateur architect. He was on friendly terms with Lord Burlington whose Palladian principles he did his best to follow (in his portrait a volume on *Palladian Architecture* stands beside him on a table). It was in the Palladian style that he rebuilt the family house Rokeby. For his father-in-law, Lord Carlisle, he designed the west wing of Castle Howard. He was also the architect of various other buildings (see H. M. Colvin, *English Architects*, 1954, pp. 509–11). Robinson was Governor of Barbadoes from 1742 to 1747. Frans van der Mijn (or Myn), a Dutch painter, worked in Amsterdam, The Hague, and in London, where he exhibited at the Free Society between 1761 and 1772.
Lent by the Hon. Lady Cary.

86 Library Table

30 × 53 × 30 in. Design attributed to William Kent, *c.* 1735–40. Carved consoles headed by lion masks terminating in paw feet, at angles and flanking arched kneehole.
Lent by the Duke of Bedford.

87 Tapestry: Meleager Delivering the Boar's Head to Atalanta

Silk and wool on woollen warp. 108 × 147 in. Woven in Antwerp for the English market, *c.* 1700. Signed: *M.W.* Exh: Birmingham, *English Tapestries*, 1951, No. 39. Lit: H. C. Marillier, *English*

Tapestries of the Eighteenth Century, London 1930, p. 86. One of a
set of three, of which the two others are Nos. 54 and 78. The initials
M.W. are usually associated with Michel Wauters, the Flemish weaver.
Lent by the Duke of Buccleuch.

88 Pair of Parcel-gilt Mahogany Pedestals

H. 46½ in. Designed by William Kent, *c.* 1740. Carved with drapery
swags and acanthus leaves. Lit: *D.E.F.*, III, p. 160, fig. 5: p. 159.
Lent by T. Cottrell-Dormer, Esq.

89 Carved and Gilt Oak Settee

39 × 72 × 31 in. By James Miller, *c.* 1760. Scroll legs, carved with
acanthus foliage, scaling and "money-moulding", ending in volutes;
covered in velvet of later date. *Cf.* No. 17.
Lent by the Earl of Leicester.

90 Carved and Gilt Gesso Side-table

34 × 48 × 24 in., *c.* 1735–40. Cabriole legs, carved with female masks,
ending in dolphins' heads; frieze centring in scroll pendant; top
decorated with oak leaves and acorns.
Lent by Mrs. David Gubbay.

SIR GODFREY KNELLER (1646 or 1649–1723)
91 The 1st Duke of Marlborough

Canvas. 36½ × 29 in. Inscribed on the back of the lining canvas:
*His Grace the Duke of Marlborough. Painted by Sr Godfrey Kneller
soon after the Battle of Ramillies 17.. when Flanders and Brabant
surrendr'd.* (May 1706.) Coll: Earls of Chichester, to whom much
of the property of the sitter's eldest daughter descended. In the
centre is Marlborough, in armour and wearing the blue ribbon of the
Garter; on the left Hercules with clubs and key, and a woman offering
the Duke a model of a citadel; on the right, War beneath the horse's
hooves. Victory or Fame stoops from the clouds to crown the Duke
with laurel. Presumably a sketch for a full-scale allegorical painting,
which seems however never to have been carried out, to celebrate the
victory of the Duke and his allies over the French at Ramillies in
1706.
Lent by the National Portrait Gallery.

BAROQUE

SIR JAMES THORNHILL (1675–1734)

92 Scene from the Life of St. Paul: St. Paul preaching at Athens

Canvas. 30 × 20 in. See No. 47.

Lent by the Dean and Chapter of St. Paul's Cathedral.

SIR JAMES THORNHILL (1675–1734)

93 Scene from the Life of St. Paul: Burning of the Books at Ephesus

Canvas. 30 × 20 in. See No. 47.

Lent by the Dean and Chapter of St. Paul's Cathedral.

94 Mahogany Cabinet on Chest of Drawers

96 × 56 × 20¾ in., *c.* 1730. Four corner pilasters with gilt capitals, surmounted by swan-neck pediment; drawers below contained within four terminal busts of Greek poets; apron centring in shell and acanthus decoration, claw-and-ball feet. Lit: P. MacQuoid, *English Furniture . . . in the Lady Lever Art Gallery*, London 1928, No. 289, Pl. 72.

Lent by the Lady Lever Art Gallery.

SIR JAMES THORNHILL (1675–1734)

95 Scene from the Life of St. Paul: St. Paul before Agrippa

Canvas. 30 × 20 in. See No. 47.

Lent by the Dean and Chapter of St. Paul's Cathedral.

SIR JAMES THORNHILL (1675–1734)

96 Scene from the Life of St. Paul: The Shipwreck at Melita

Canvas. 30 × 20 in. See No. 47.

Lent by the Dean and Chapter of St. Paul's Cathedral.

GALLERY IX
ROCOCO

ALLAN RAMSAY (1713–1784)

97   Caroline, 1st Baroness Holland

Canvas.   40 × 48 in.   Lit: Earl of Ilchester, *The Home of the Hollands*, 1937, p. 71; Sir James L. Caw, "Allan Ramsay", *Walpole Society*, Vol. 25, 1936–37, repr. Pl. XXX; A. Smart, *Allan Ramsay*, London 1952, p. 133.   There are other examples of Ramsay's later portraits which might better illustrate his affinity with the French rococo artists such as Nattier.   But this portrait has been chosen as it is the only one which shows a lady with furniture which is rococo in character.   The sitter, Lady Caroline Lennox (1723–74), the eldest daughter of the 2nd Duke of Richmond, married in 1744 Henry Fox and became the mother of Charles James Fox.   She was gazetted Baroness Holland in her own right in 1752.
Lent by the Earl of Ilchester.

98   Mahogany Writing-table

$39\frac{1}{2} \times 52 \times 33\frac{1}{2}$ in., *c.* 1765.   Lower portion based on a design in the 3rd Edition of Chippendale's *Director*, 1762, Pl. LXXII.   Ormolu mounts; side drawers of lower stage decorated with parquetry veneer and knee-hole recess carved with acanthus.   Lit: *D.E.F.*, III, p. 254, fig. 32.
Lent by the Dowager Marchioness of Bristol.

99   Worcester Porcelain: Pair of Fruit Baskets

H. 3 in., *c.* 1770 (Dr. Wall period).   Unmarked.
Lent by A. Wyndham Green, Esq.

100   Worcester Porcelain: Covered Dish and Stand

H. 5 in., *c.* 1770 (Dr. Wall period).   Unmarked.
Lent by A. Wyndham Green, Esq.

MARCELLUS LAROON, THE YOUNGER (1679–1774)

101   The Duke of Montagu's Levée

Canvas.   36 × 29 in.   Lit: *Southill, a Regency House*, London 1951, pp. 46–7, Pl. 63.   The background is predominantly Baroque, but the nervous staccato brushwork of Laroon is essentially Rococo in character. The title has been questioned and it has been suggested that the scene represents Old Montagu House in Bloomsbury, with the 2nd Duke of Montagu (1690–1749). The house was built by the 1st Duke, and rebuilt by him with little alteration after it was destroyed by fire in 1686. It was bought by the Government in 1753 to house the British Museum and almost one hundred years later was demolished and replaced by the present building. On the basis that four drawings (said to represent musical parties at Montagu House) are all dated between 1733 and 1736 it is possible that the picture belongs to these years.

Lent by Major Simon Whitbread.

THOMAS GAINSBOROUGH, R.A. (1727–1788)

102 Sir Richard and Lady Neave

Canvas. 87 × 59 in. Exh: Cardiff, 1951, No. 27. Lit: E. K. Waterhouse, *Preliminary Check List of Portraits by Thomas Gainsborough*, Walpole Society, XXXIII, 1953, p. 80. Sir Richard Neave, 1st Bt. (1731–1814), of Dagnam Park, Essex, and his wife Frances (d. 1830), daughter of John Bristow, of Quidenham Hall, Norfolk. They were married in 1761. (Dated by Waterhouse (*op. cit.*), *c.* 1764–65.)

Lent by Sir Arundel Neave, Bt.

103 Mahogany Commode

32 × 42 × 25 in. Attributed to Thomas Chippendale. After a design dated 1753 in the 1st Edition of the *Director*, 1754, Pl. XLIII. Cabriole legs and interlacing scrolls between drawers. A commode identical in appearance, but with dummy drawers enclosing cupboards, was exhibited at Ormeley Lodge, Ham Common, *Masterpieces of British Art and Craftsmanship*, 1954, No. 15 (Anon. lender). Lit: *D.E.F.*, II, p. 113, fig. 7: p. 110.

Lent by John A. Arnold-Forster, Esq.

104 Chelsea Porcelain: Pair of Candelabra with Stag Hunt and Leopard Hunt

H. 15¾ in., *c.* 1765. Mark: gold anchor.

Lent by Sir Harold Wernher, Bt.

105 Carved and Gilt Bracket

19 × 11 in., *c.* 1755. Shelf supported on eagle and rococo scrollwork.

Lent by Major Edward Compton.

WILLIAM HOGARTH (1697–1764)

106 George II and his Family

Canvas. 25 × 30 in. Coll: bt. by H.M. The Queen, 1955. (For previous owners and literature, see Arts Council Exhibition Catalogue.) Exh: Arts Council, London, *William Hogarth*, 1951, No. 21. Represented in the picture are the Duke of Cumberland, George II, Queen Caroline, Princesses Louisa, Mary, Princess Royal, Princesses Amelia, Caroline, Prince of Wales. A smaller alternative version is in the National Gallery of Ireland. In 1733 Vertue writes (III, p. 68) that Hogarth had begun a picture of the Royal Family, the sketch having been made.

Lent by Her Majesty The Queen (Windsor Castle).

107 Pair of Mahogany Tea-kettle Stands

H. 32, Diam. 14 in., *c.* 1765. Hexagonal tops, carved with scrolls and paterae and enclosed by lattice-work galleries. Lit: *D.E.F.*, III, p. 157, fig. 6.

Lent by the Earl of Radnor.

FRANCIS HAYMAN, R.A. (1708–1776)

108 May Day

Canvas. 13¾ × 17½ in. A model for the large painting formerly in Vauxhall Gardens, executed soon after 1740, and now in the Victoria and Albert Museum. (See Lawrence Gowing, "Hogarth, Hayman and the Vauxhall Decorations", *Burlington Magazine*, XCV, 1952, pp. 4 ff., Pl. 16; see also p. 142.)

Lent by J. Byam Shaw, Esq.

JOHN ZOFFANY, R.A. (1735–1810)

109 Charles Rheinhold as Hawthorn in "Love in a Village"

Canvas. 25¼ × 19¾ in. Lit: C. K. Adams, *Catalogue of the Garrick Club Pictures*, London 1936, No. 100. This picture is included as it depicts a typical rococo looking-glass in its eighteenth-century setting. Looking-glasses of this kind, which were intended for moderate-sized houses, are comparatively common compared with the more elaborate examples in this Exhibition. Charles Rheinhold (1737–1815) was primarily known as a singer. He was a pupil of Handel's and his long career at Marylebone Gardens started in 1759. In 1783 he was appointed organist of St. George's, Bloomsbury.

Lent by the Garrick Club.

ROCOCO

THOMAS GAINSBOROUGH, R.A. (1727-1788)

110 Musidora

Canvas. Painted oval. 73 × 59½ in. Coll: Mrs. Gainsborough's sale, 11th April 1797, Lot 82; presented to the National Gallery by Robert Vernon in 1847; transferred to the Tate Gallery, 1919. Exh: Tate Gallery (Arts Council) *Thomas Gainsborough*, 1953, No. 61. Very late unfinished work (Waterhouse). The subject, of Musidora observed by young Damon while bathing in a wood, comes from Thomson's *Seasons*.
Lent by the Tate Gallery.

111 Mahogany Commode

33 × 54 × 26 in., *c.* 1760. Serpentine front; escutcheons and handle plates of pierced brass; consoles at angles and apron carved with rococo motifs; legs finishing in volutes.
Lent by the Hon. Mrs. Ionides.

MARCELLUS LAROON, THE YOUNGER (1679-1774)

112 Two Dancers

Canvas. 35½ × 27¼ in. Exh: 45 Park Lane, 1938, No. 81.
Lent by Sir Osbert Sitwell, Bt.

113 Pair of Carved and Gilt Girandoles

H. 56½ in., *c.* 1762. Closely follow a design in the 3rd Edition of Chippendale's *Director*, 1762, Pl. CLXXVIII (centre). Rococo decoration with *putti*, urns of flowers and acanthus scrolls; two candle branches.
Lent by the Marquess of Anglesey.

114 Mahogany Bureau

84 × 37 × 30 in. By William Vile for Queen Charlotte, 1761. Rococo and *bombé* base; upper portion enclosed with carved lattice-work in Chinese taste, headed by recessed canopy supporting Royal Crown; two top drawer-fronts let down, forming writing flap. Lit: H. Clifford Smith, *Buckingham Palace*, London 1931, pp. 73 and 278, Pls. 62, 63. *D.E.F.*, I, p. 148, figs. 54, 55: p. 146.
Lent by Her Majesty The Queen (Buckingham Palace).

115 Worcester Porcelain: Six Examples from a Dessert Service

c. 1765. Unmarked: Earl Manvers Pattern.
Lent by Sir Harold Wernher, Bt.

116 Pair of Carved and Gilt Girandoles

H. 28 in., *c.* 1755. In form of trees, with foliage supporting birds; three candle branches with nozzles of gilded brass.
Lent by Mrs. David Gubbay.

117 Pair of Carved and Gilt Brackets

H. 18 in. Attributed to Thomas Chippendale, *c.* 1755. Shelfs supported on cranes with outspread wings; C-scrolls and foliage. Lit: *D.E.F.*, I, p. 119, fig. 13.
Lent by the Duke of Atholl.

118 Mahogany China Cabinet

87 × 38 × 15 in., *c.* 1750. Top portion with three doors, centre with arched top, cornice mouldings carved with leaves; lower portion fitted with drawers bordered with key-pattern decoration. Doors probably originally fitted with mirrors, changed to glass when collecting porcelain became fashionable. Exh: Ormeley Lodge, *Masterpieces of British Art and Craftsmanship*, 1954, No. 19. (Repr.)
Lent by the Duke of Northumberland.

119 Pair of Silver Tea-caddies

H. 5¾ in. By Abraham Portal, 1754. *Bombé* shape; flower on lids, Chinese figures and rococo scrolling on sides.
Lent by the Hon. Mrs. Ionides.

120 Silver Tea-caddy

H. 6½ in. By Alexander Johnson, 1755. *Bombé* shape, embossed in chinoiserie style.
Lent by Ronald A. Lee, Esq.

121 Pair of Silver Tea-caddies

H. 6 in. By Samuel Taylor, 1762. Pear-shaped; rococo designs with Chinese figures.
Lent by the Hon. Mrs. Ionides.

122 Sugar Vase

H. 6½ in. By Samuel Taylor, 1762. Pear-shaped; rococo design with Chinese figures. From the same set as No. 121.
Lent by the Hon. Mrs. Ionides.

123   Silver Coffee-pot

H. 12 in.   By Francis Crump, 1761.   Pear-shaped with Chinese figure as knop of lid; figures, shell-work, cartouche and rococo scrolling on sides.

Lent by the Hon. Mrs. Ionides.

124   Three Silver Oval Dishes

10½ × 8 in.   By Paul de Lamerie, 1752.   Shaped ovals; edges with shell-work, child masks, flowers and rococo scrolls.

Lent by the Hon. Mrs. Ionides.

125   Silver Tea-pot

H. 7 in.   By Peter and Ann Bateman, 1796.   Oval; Chinese figure as knop of lid; figures, pagodas, willow trees and rococo cartouche on sides.

Lent by the Hon. Mrs. Ionides.

126   Pair of Silver Tea-caddies

H. 6 in.   By Samuel Taylor, 1763.   Rectangular; leaf-shaped pagoda lids, bells at corners; Chinese figures, vases of flowers and rococo cartouches on sides.

Lent by the Hon. Mrs. Ionides.

127   Silver Tea-caddy

H. 6¾ in.   By Samuel Taylor, 1763.   Rectangular back and front embossed with rococo ornament, ends with chinoiserie.

Lent by the Hon. Mrs. Ionides.

128   Silver-gilt Tea-caddy

H. 5¼ in.   By Paul de Lamerie, 1746.   One of a pair; rectangular, embossed with chinoiserie rural scenes.

Lent by the Worshipful Company of Goldsmiths.

G. B. PIAZZETTA (1682–1754), CANALETTO (1697–1768) and G. B. CIMAROLI (Active 1st half of XVIIIth Century)

129   Allegorical Tomb in Honour of Lord Chief Justice Somers

Canvas.   92 × 56 in.   Lit: F. J. B. Watson, "An Allegorical Painting by Canaletto, Piazzetta, and Cimaroli," *Burlington Magazine*, XCV, 1953, pp. 362–5, fig. 1; W. G. Constable, Letter in *Burlington Magazine*, XCVI, 1954, p. 154.   Commissioned by Owen McSwinny. This painting forms part of the series of Allegorical Tombs in Honour

of recently deceased Englishmen of note (for history see under No. 135).
It is mentioned in the pamphlet "To the Ladies and Gentlemen of
Taste . . ." Our knowledge of the artists employed to paint it is due
to an MS. letter (in the archives at Goodwood) from McSwinny to the
Duke of Richmond dated 8th March 1722, in which their names are
mentioned and it is implied that the work is nearing completion.
It is thus the earliest known work by Canaletto, preceding any of his
known views of Venice. Presumably Canaletto was responsible for
the architectural part, Cimaroli for the landscape and Piazzetta for
the figures. The Duke of Richmond does not, in the event, appear
to have acquired the painting; it was certainly not in the Goodwood
dining-room.
Lent by the Earl of Plymouth.

130 Pair of Carved and Gilt Console Tables

34 × 46 × 24 in., *c.* 1750. Tops carved in low relief; rococo ornament; scrolled cabriole supports, aprons of pierced acanthus foliage
centring in *putti* masks; on plinths, scrolls and foliage. Lit: *D.E.F.*,
III, p. 292, fig. 53: pp. 297–8.
Lent by the Leeds Art Gallery (Temple Newsam House).

131 Pair of Mirrors in Carved and Gilt Frames

76 × 47 in., *c.* 1755–60. Carved with long-necked birds and rococo
detail.
Lent by Capt. J. B. E. Radcliffe.

FRANCESCO FERNANDI, CALLED IMPERIALI (*op.* 1723–37)
132 Allegorical Tomb in Honour of King George I

Canvas. 70 × 90 in. Coll: Duke of Richmond. Lit: Vertue V
(*Walpole Society*, Vol. XXVI, pp. 149–50); *Connoisseur*, XXXIII,
No. 333 (May 1929), p. 264, Pl. VI (with an attribution to Hubert
Robert). For a general history of the series of which this forms a
part, see under No. 135. This painting was hanging between the doors
of the dining-room at Goodwood when Vertue saw it. Alone amongst
the series of Tombs it is horizontal in shape; the rest are vertical with
feigned arched tops. It is listed in the pamphlet "To the Ladies and
Gentlemen of Taste . . ." Vertue (*op. cit.*) describes it in detail and
adds that it was "painted by Fr. Imperiali". An upright version of
the composition with the conventional feigned arched top was exhibited in Berlin in 1927 together with a version of the Allegorical
Tomb in Honour of William III. (Information kindly supplied by
Mr. Francis Watson.)
Lent by Viscount Kemsley.

133 Carved and Gilt Side-table

$38\frac{1}{2} \times 67\frac{1}{2} \times 36$ in., *c.* 1745–50.   Brecchia marble top; rococo ornament; scrolled legs headed by satyr masks, pierced apron centring in basket of fruit.   Lit: *D.E.F.*, III, p. 290, fig. 47: p. 292.
Lent by the Leeds Art Gallery (Temple Newsam House).

LOUIS FRANÇOIS ROUBILIAC (1702/5–1762)

134 Joseph Wilton, R.A., 1722–1803.

Plaster bust.   H. 33 in.   Inscribed on base: *Joseph Wilton Esq*[r]
RA | died Nov[r.] *25th 1803 | this Bust, by Roubilliac, is presented to the Royal Academy | by his daughter Lady Chambers.*   Presented to the Royal Academy by Lady Chambers, 1824.   Exh: Society of Artists, 1761, No. 154; R.A. Winter 1951–52, No. 17.
Lent by the Royal Academy of Arts.

MARCO AND SEBASTIANO RICCI (1676–1729: 1659–1734)

135 Allegorical Tomb in Honour of the Duke of Devonshire

Canvas. 90×58 in.   Coll: Duke of Richmond; Christie's, 14th June 1946, Lot 84 (as Lo Brun, *Fall of Constantine*).   Lit: Vertue V (*Walpole Society*, Vol. XXVI, pp. 149–50).

In 1713 Owen McSwinny, the Irish impresario of the opera, was forced into bankruptcy and fled abroad.   About 1720 he took up residence with Joseph Smith at Venice.   In order to make money he commissioned some of the leading Venetian and Bolognese rococo artists, and also one or two young artists as yet unestablished, like Canaletto, to paint, sometimes in collaboration, a series of allegorical tombs in honour of recently deceased Englishmen of note.   Details of the scheme were published by McSwinny in a pamphlet "To the Ladies and Gentlemen of Taste . . ."

Between 1720 and 1730 about two dozen tombs were completed, of which ten were quickly sold to the 2nd Duke of Richmond for Goodwood, where Vertue saw them in June 1747 (*op. cit.* above). He described No. 135 as "painted by Ricci" and Mr. Francis Watson, who has kindly supplied the information about the tombs, has plausibly suggested that it is, in fact, the work of both Sebastiano and Marco Ricci, the former being responsible for the figures.
Lent by the Victoria and Albert Museum.

PHILIPPE MERCIER (1689–1760)

136 A Fishing Party

Canvas. 33 × 39 in. Mercier, who was an imitator of Watteau, was largely responsible for introducing into English Society the small-scale conversation piece derived from the *Assemblée Galante*. Mercier's style with its rococo elements and Gallic vivacity had an influence on a number of English artists.
Lent by M. Wickham-Boynton, Esq.

137 Mahogany Work Table

31½ × 40 × 30 in. By William Vile for Queen Charlotte, 1763. Shaped frieze ornamented with fretwork; cabriole legs carved with acanthus and ending in volutes. Lit: H. Clifford Smith, *Buckingham Palace*, London 1931, p. 78, Pl. 64. *D.E.F.* III, p. 321, fig. 3: p. 320.
Lent by Her Majesty The Queen (Buckingham Palace).

138 Chelsea Porcelain: Oviform Vase

H. 15 in., *c.* 1765. Mark: gold anchor.
Lent by Sir Harold Wernher, Bt.

GALLERY VIII

ROCOCO

LOUIS FRANÇOIS ROUBILIAC (1702/5–1762)

139 Alexander Pope

Marble bust. H. 18½ in. Inscribed on back: *A. Pope AE^{is} 52. L. F. Roubiliac, SC^{it} AD VIVUM 1740*; and in front: *UNI AEQUUS VIRTUTI ATQUE EJUS AMICIS.* Alexander Pope (1688–1744), poet and critic. Other busts of Pope by Roubiliac are (1) dated 1738, in the Leeds Art Gallery; (2) 1741?, in the National Portrait Gallery.
Lent by the Earl Fitzwilliam.

140 Mahogany Pedestal

H. 60 in., *c.* 1750. Shaft carved with eagle's head and elaborate rococo detail. Coll: Powis Castle.
Lent by Brigadier the Viscount Downe.

141 Pair of Arabesque Tapestries

Silk and wool on woollen warp. 126 × 198 in. By Joshua Morris (working *c.* 1710–30). Lit: H. C. Marillier, *English Tapestries of the Eighteenth Century*, London 1930, p. 10.
Lent by Viscount Cobham.

142 Mahogany Chair

39 × 25 × 20 in., *c.* 1762. The splat closely follows a design in the 3rd Edition of Chippendale's *Director*, 1762, Pl. XIV. Alternative patterns for front legs are given, one of which has been adopted. Bow-shaped top-rail, gothic motifs in splat tracery; shallow apron and scrolled legs. The chair may be attributed to Chippendale's firm. Lit: *D.E.F.*, I, p. 280, fig. 172: p. 282.
Lent by the Duke of Norfolk.

143 Pair of Parcel-gilt Mahogany Stands

H. 43, Diam. 14 in., *c.* 1755. Top, pierced and gadrooned; fluted shafts carved with acanthus; cabriole legs finishing in volutes. Coll: apparently those formerly at Raby Castle, Co. Durham. Lit: O. Brackett, *English Furniture Illustrated*, revised by H. Clifford Smith, 1950, Pl. CLXVIII.
Lent by Mrs. Geoffrey Hart.

144 Mahogany Commode

36 × 52 × 27 in.   Attributed to William Vile, *c.* 1750.   One of a pair. Serpentine form, with lifting tops and false drawers; child-headed consoles; ovals on panels with acanthus foliage.   Lit: D.E.F., II, p. 112, fig. 4: p. 109.
Lent by the Duke of Richmond and Gordon.

145 Silver Tureen

H. 12½ in.   By William Cripps, 1756.   Oval, with applied cast ornament representing game; with arms of Other Lewis, 4th Earl of Plymouth.
Lent by the Earl of Plymouth.

146 Mahogany Armchair

38½ × 28 × 22 in., *c.* 1760.   Curved arm supports and cabriole legs, finishing in volutes, carved with foliage; shaped seat-rail; damask cover of later date.
Lent by Mrs. Geoffrey Hart.

LOUIS FRANÇOIS ROUBILIAC (1702/5–1762)

147 Isaac Ware

Marble bust.   H. 21 in.   Coll: Lady Fitzgerald.   Lit: H. M. Colvin, "Roubiliac's Bust of Isaac Ware", *Burlington Magazine*, XCVII, 1955, p. 151.   Isaac Ware, who is said to have started life as a chimney-sweeper's boy, was reputed to have been patronised by Lord Burlington.   In 1729 he became Clerk of the Works at Windsor, in 1733 at Greenwich and in 1736 he was appointed secretary to the Board of Works.   Between 1750 and 1758 he acted as draughtsman for the building of the Horse Guards to Kent's designs.   He was the architect of Chesterfield House and of Wrotham Park, Middlesex, which is his most important surviving architectural work.   He died in 1766. As Mr. Colvin points out (*op. cit.*), Roubiliac made two different busts of Ware: the first, according to Vertue, in 1741; the second, a clay model (engraved by J. T. Smith) of which this is the marble version, after 1755.
Lent by Major Richard Wellesley.

148 Pair of Carved and Gilt Wall Candle-brackets

H. 47 in., *c.* 1750.   For three lights; each with cedar tree, two columns and entablature backed by mirror; figures at outer sides; rococo bases.   Lit: P. MacQuoid, *English Furniture . . . in the Lady Lever Art Gallery*, London 1928, No. 108, Pl. 34.
Lent by the Lady Lever Art Gallery.

149 Mahogany Cabinet

85 × 60 × 20 in. Attributed to William Vile, *c.* 1755–60. Breakfront, carved with Chinese and rococo ornament; central "broken" pediment, perforated galleries; lower frieze surmounted by pagoda moulding; carved laurel wreaths on panels of lower stage. Lit: *D.E.F.*, I, p. 188, fig. 49: p. 185.
Lent by Mrs. H. Scudamore.

150 Longton Hall Porcelain: A Youth

H. 9½ in., *c.* 1758. Unmarked.
Lent by the Cecil Higgins Museum, Bedford.

151 Chelsea Porcelain: Pair of Sea Horses

H. 5⅞ in., *c.* 1755. Unmarked.
Lent by the Cecil Higgins Museum, Bedford.

152 Derby Porcelain: Shepherd and Shepherdess (A Pair)

H. 8 in., *c.* 1765. Unmarked.
Lent by the Cecil Higgins Museum, Bedford.

153 Bow Porcelain: Dancing Youth and Girl (A Pair)

H. 7½ in., *c.* 1765. Mark: anchor and dagger in red, "A" in blue.
Lent by the Cecil Higgins Museum, Bedford.

154 Derby Porcelain: Youth with Pipe and Tabor

H. 8⅜ in., *c.* 1765. Patch marks on base.
Lent by the Cecil Higgins Museum, Bedford.

155 Bow Porcelain: Two Children Dancing

H. 8⅝ in., *c.* 1765. Mark: double dot.
Lent by the Cecil Higgins Museum, Bedford.

156 Bow Porcelain: Jupiter and the Eagle

H. 9 in., *c.* 1765. Mark: anchor and dagger in red, rod in blue.
Lent by the Cecil Higgins Museum, Bedford.

157 Derby Porcelain: Girl with Birdcage

H. 8¾ in., *c.* 1765. Unmarked.
Lent by the Cecil Higgins Museum, Bedford.

158 Bow Porcelain: Shepherd with Bagpipe, and Shepherdess (A Pair)
H. 10¾ in., *c.* 1765. Unmarked.
Lent by the Cecil Higgins Museum, Bedford.

159 Chelsea Porcelain: Urn Decorated with Chinoiserie Figures
H. 8½ in., 1758. Mark: red anchor, with date.
Lent by the Cecil Higgins Museum, Bedford.

160 Chelsea Porcelain: Pair of Candlestick Figures of Musicians
H. 11 in., *c.* 1765. Mark: red anchor.
Lent by the Cecil Higgins Museum, Bedford.

161 Chelsea Porcelain: Dessert Plate
Diam. 8¾ in., *c.* 1765. Mark: gold anchor.
Lent by the Cecil Higgins Museum, Bedford.

162 Derby Porcelain: "Diana".
H. 10⅜ in., *c.* 1765. Patch marks on base.
Lent by the Cecil Higgins Museum, Bedford.

163 Bow Porcelain: Youth Playing Violin and Girl Playing Flute
      (A Pair)
H. 6 in., *c.* 1760–65. Marks: double dot in blue.
Lent by the Cecil Higgins Museum, Bedford.

164 Mahogany Ribband-back Chair
40 × 28 × 26 in., *c.* 1755. One of a set; splat of interlaced ribbons,
claw-and-ball feet. Lit: *D.E.F.*, I, pp. 281–2, fig. 173.
Lent by the Hon. Rowland Winn.

165 Mahogany Chair
39 × 23 × 20 in., *c.* 1760. Pierced splat; frame and cabriole legs,
finishing in volutes, carved with rococo motifs; covered in contemporary needlework.
Lent by Mrs. David Gubbay.

166 Pair of Carved and Gilt Wall Candle-brackets
H. 41 in., *c.* 1750. For two lights; upper portions with architectural
ruins and column above scenes from *Æsop's Fables*; lower parts
decorated with rococo motifs enclosing mirror. Lit: P. MacQuoid,
English Furniture . . . in the Lady Lever Art Gallery, London 1928,
No. 147, Pl. 41.
Lent by the Lady Lever Art Gallery.

167 Mahogany Cabinet

94 × 51 × 21 in. Attributed to William Vile, c. 1755. "Broken" pediment above frieze supported on consoles and carved with swags of foliage; lower portion frieze with Vitruvian scroll; centre flanked by `consoles; panels carved with ovals clasped by acanthus foliage. Coll: said to have come from Charlemont House, Dublin.
Lent by Lord Rockley.

168 Chelsea Porcelain: Pair of Vases and Covers

H. 12¼ in., c. 1765. Mark: gold anchor.
Lent by Sir Harold Wernher, Bt.

169 Plymouth Porcelain: Cupids

H. 5½, c. 1768–70. Unmarked.
Lent by Sir Harold Wernher, Bt.

170 Bow Porcelain: Pair of Parrots

H. 6¾ and 7½ in., c. 1765. Mark: impressed "T" (the modeller, Tebo).
Lent by Sir Harold Wernher, Bt.

171 Chelsea Porcelain: Pair of Dessert Plates

Diam. 8½ in., c. 1765. Mark: gold anchor.
Lent by Sir Harold Wernher, Bt.

172 Chelsea Porcelain: Pair of Trumpet-shaped Vases

H. 13¼ in., c. 1765. Mark: gold anchor.
Lent by Sir Harold Wernher, Bt.

LOUIS FRANÇOIS ROUBILIAC (1702/5–1762)

173 George Frederick Handel

Marble bust. H. 28 in. Signed: *Roubiliac F.* Inscribed: *Handel Aetatis Suae 54, MDCCXXXIX.* Coll: presented by J. C. Smith to George III in 1773. Lit: K. A. Esdaile, *Louis François Roubiliac,* London 1928, p. 51. George Frederick Handel (1685–1759). It was owing to the patronage of Lord Burlington that he was received at the Court of George I. The terracotta model for the bust is in the National Portrait Gallery, London.
Lent by Her Majesty The Queen (Windsor Castle).

174 Pair of Arabesque Tapestries

Silk and wool on woollen warp. 126 × 42 in. By Joshua Morris (working *c.* 1710–30). Lit: H. C. Marillier, *English Tapestries of the Eighteenth Century*, London 1930, p. 10.
Lent by Viscount Cobham.

175 Mahogany Armchair

43 × 28 × 22 in., *c.* 1760. Scrolled legs and arm supports in rococo taste; back and seat covered with contemporary needlework.
Lent by Mrs. David Gubbay.

176 Mahogany Kneehole Writing Desk

33½ × 50 × 26½ in. Attributed to Thomas Chippendale, *c.* 1760. Top veneered in partridge wood with satinwood banding; canted corners with carved swags and Crewe crest; carved mahogany handle plates on satinwood. Coll: Lord Crewe. Lit: *Leeds Arts Calendar*, Vol. 6. No. 21, pp. 6–7 (Repd.).
Lent by the Leeds Art Gallery (Temple Newsam House).

177 Silver-gilt Two-handled Cup and Cover

H. 14¼ in. By William Kidney, 1740. Bell-shaped body, decorated with cartouches supported by symbolical figures with handles in form of Bacchanalian figures; cover surmounted by bust of Silenus; with arms of Lovell of Norfolk impaling Porter of Worcestershire.
Lent by the Worshipful Company of Goldsmiths.

178 Pair of Mirrors in Carved and Gilt Frames

65 × 47 in., *c.* 1755. One of a set of four formerly at Kensington Palace; rococo framework with floral pendants; on the lateral scrolls, agitated storks. Lit: *D.E.F.*, II, p. 340, fig. 76: p. 337.
Lent by Her Majesty The Queen (Windsor Castle).

179 Pair of Mahogany Chairs

42 × 24 × 20 in., *c.* 1750. From a set of seven. Crestings centring in pagodas, backs framed by foliated branches, seat-rails ornamented with acanthus and pagoda motifs; legs with grotesque carving, terminating in dolphins' heads; backs and seats upholstered in blue and grey silk of later date. Lit: P. MacQuoid, *English Furniture . . . in the Lady Lever Art Gallery*, London 1928, No. 155, Pl. 47.
Lent by the Lady Lever Art Gallery.

180 Mahogany Writing Cabinet

94 × 46 × 30 in. Attributed to an immigrant craftsman, possibly Peter Langlois, *c.* 1745. Serpentine front and sides; cupboard doors and drawers inlaid in brass with arabesques; ormolu rococo mounts. The technique of inlaid metal was first practised in England by Gerrit Jensen in late Stuart times. Lit: *D.E.F.*, I, p. 194, fig. 45: p. 140.
Lent by Arthur Bull, Esq.

181 Mahogany Commode Chest of Drawers

36 × 62 × 27 in., *c.* 1760. Serpentine front; five drawers; gilt-brass handles in rococo taste; edge of top with egg-and-dart moulding; canted corners carved with trusses, foliage and scrolls; between drawers key-pattern, rosettes and other motifs.
Lent by the Lady Elizabeth Byng.

182 Silver-gilt Cup

H. 13½ in. By Paul de Lamerie, 1739. Bell-shaped body, strapwork of fruit and masks, domed cover with floral ornament; with arms of John Gawler Bridge.
Lent by the Worshipful Company of Goldsmiths.

183 Mahogany Pole-screen

H. 67½ in., *c.* 1750. Frame, shaft and tripod support elaborately carved with stalactite ornament and other rococo motifs; the panel of tapestry, perhaps Beauvais.
Lent by Mrs. David Gubbay.

LOUIS FRANÇOIS ROUBILIAC (1702/5–1762)

184 Lord Ligonier

Marble bust. H. 27 in. Signed: *L. F. Roubiliac Sc. ad Vivum.* Lit: K. A. Esdaile, *Louis François Roubiliac*, London 1928, pp. 91–2, Pl. XXIV. John, Earl Ligonier (1680–1770), first served under Marlborough; in 1712 Governor of Fort St. Philip, Minorca; in 1720 given command of the "Ligoniers" (now 7th Dragoon Guards). K.B. after Dettingen; C.-in-C. British troops in the Austrian Netherlands. Captured, and later employed as intermediary in negotiations ending in the Peace of Aix-la-Chapelle. In 1766 created Earl and Field-Marshal. Gunnis (*Dictionary of British Sculptors*, London 1953, p. 330) dates this bust *c.* 1750. The terracotta model is in the National Portrait Gallery.
Lent by Her Majesty The Queen (Windsor Castle).

185 Pair of Arabesque Tapestries

Silk and wool on woollen warp. 126 × 90 in. By Joshua Morris (working *c.* 1710–30). Lit: H. C. Marillier, *English Tapestries of the Eighteenth Century*, London 1930, p. 10.
Lent by Viscount Cobham.

186 Carved and Gilt Chest

33 × 38 × 21½ in. Attributed to William Vile; probably supplied to the 1st Lord Folkestone by the firm of Vile and Cobb, *c.* 1755–60. Access to upper part gained by lifting top, which has an inset panel of oriental lacquer; front elaborately carved with rococo ornament on a diapered ground; stiles with satyr masks and pendants of fruit and flowers; doors enclosing mahogany drawers. Lit: *D.E.F.*, II, pp. 24–5, fig. 49.
Lent by the Earl of Radnor.

187 Pair of Silver-gilt Candlesticks

H. 10 in. By George Wickes, 1737. Baluster stems chased with masks; octagonal bases.
Lent by the Worshipful Company of Goldsmiths.

188 Bracket Clock

29½ × 15½ × 10 in. By John Ellicott, *c.* 1750. Figured mahogany, with mounts of silver-gilt. Coll: said to have been in the possession of the Empress Catherine of Russia.
Lent by Lord Kenyon.

189 Mahogany Kettle-stand

H. 21½: Diam. 11¼ in., *c.* 1750. Shaft carved and fluted; tripod legs carved with foliage ending in claw-and-ball feet; top with shaped edge carved with nulling.
Lent by Mrs. Geoffrey Hart.

190 Arabesque Carpet

192 × 144 in. By Claud Passavant, a French immigrant, adapting a traditional Savonnerie design. Signed and dated: *Exon. 1758*. Knotted carpet; central panel with sunflower; cube-pattern field with scattered flowers; outer border with columns and shells. Despite the date, the survival of baroque motifs is apparent. A similar carpet, made in Exeter by Claud Passavant (1757), is in the Victoria and Albert Museum. Lit: *D.E.F.*, I, p. 214.
Lent by John Wyndham, Esq.

191 Pair of Mahogany Winecoolers

19 × 17 × 12 in., *c.* 1734. Supported on cabriole legs with paw feet; top moulding gadrooned; frieze carved with scroll-work. Linings, lifting handles and inset coat of arms (of Bentinck quartering Noel and Wriothesley) in silver. Exh.: Ormeley Lodge, *Masterpieces of British Art and Craftsmanship*, 1954, No. 144 (Repr.).
Lent by the Duke of Portland.

192 Mahogany Tripod Table

H. 27½, Diam. 32 in., *c.* 1750. Border of top carved with flowers and rococo scroll-work; shaft with fluting and foliage; cabriole supports with claw-and-ball feet.
Lent by Mrs. David Gubbay.

193 Silver-gilt Salver

Diam. 22 in. By Thomas Farren, 1740. One of a pair; round, with elaborate rococo border decorated with masks; with arms of the Company.
Lent by the Worshipful Company of Goldsmiths.

194 Pair of Mahogany Armchairs

39 × 28 × 27 in., *c.* 1755. Part of a set; arms and pillar legs carved with lattice pattern, foliage and flowers; seat-rail with acanthus foliage; pierced brackets, guttae feet; covered in silk damask of later date.
Lent by the Shaftesbury Estates Company.

SAMUEL SCOTT (1703–1772)

195 Lord Anson's Victory off Cape Finisterre, 1747

Canvas. 40 × 70 in. Signed and dated: *S. Scott 1749*. Exh: Guildhall, *Paintings and Drawings by Samuel Scott*, 1955, No. 5. Gilt frame elaborately carved with rushes, C-scrolls, lattice-work and rococo ornament; marine emblems at base and cresting, with head of Neptune.
Lent by the United Service Club.

196 Mahogany Bookcase

105 × 103½ × 26½ in. By Vile and Cobb for Queen Charlotte, 1762. Classical elevation with projecting centre and two wings; entablature surmounted by "broken" pediment, on four Corinthian columns; panels of cupboards in lower portion carved with rococo scroll-work with Garter Star forming central decoration. Lit: H. Clifford Smith, *Buckingham Palace*, London 1931, pp. 78, 278–9. Pl. 66. *D.E.F.* I, p. 86, Pl. I.
Lent by Her Majesty The Queen (Buckingham Palace).

197   **Plymouth Porcelain: Pair of Phœnixes**
H. 8¼ in, *c.* 1768–70.   Unmarked.
Lent by Sir Harold Wernher, Bt.

198   **Chelsea Porcelain: Boy and Girl Musician (A Pair)**
H. 10 in.   *c.* 1765.   Unmarked.   Possibly Chelsea-Derby.
Lent by Sir Harold Wernher, Bt.

199   **Chelsea Porcelain: Shepherd and Shepherdess (A Pair)**
H. 8½ in., *c.* 1765.   Mark: gold anchor, and impressed "R".
Lent by Sir Harold Wernher, Bt.

200   **Chelsea Porcelain: Pair of Candlestick Figures of Leda and the Swan and Venus and Cupid**
H. 13 in., *c.* 1765.   Mark: gold anchor.
Lent by Sir Harold Wernher, Bt.

201   **Bow Porcelain: Summer and Autumn (A Pair)**
H. 10 in., *c.* 1765.   Mark: blue dagger.
Lent by Sir Harold Wernher, Bt.

202   **Chelsea Porcelain: Actor and Actress from the Italian Comedy (A Pair)**
H. 12½ in., *c.* 1765.   Mark: gold anchor.
Lent by Sir Harold Wernher, Bt.

203   **Chelsea Porcelain: Vauxhall Singers (A Pair)**
H. 12½ in., *c.* 1765.   Mark: gold anchor.
Lent by Sir Harold Wernher, Bt.

204   **Bow Porcelain: Pair of Figures in Eastern Dress**
H. 8¼ in., *c.* 1765.   Mark: blue dagger, red anchor and dagger (male figure); blue crescent, gold anchor and dagger (female figure).
Lent by Sir Harold Wernher, Bt.

205   **Bow Porcelain: Pair of Musicians**
H. 7 in., *c.* 1765.   Unmarked.
Lent by Sir Harold Wernher, Bt.

206   **Chelsea Porcelain: Fortune Teller and Girl**
H. 12¾ in., *c.* 1765.   Mark: gold anchor.
Lent by Sir Harold Wernher, Bt.

207   **Chelsea Porcelain: Two Lovers**
H. 12½ in, *c.* 1765.   Mark: gold anchor.
Lent by Sir Harold Wernher, Bt.

208   **Chelsea Porcelain: Pair of Flat Vases**
H. 9¾ in., *c.* 1765.   Mark: gold anchor.
Lent by Sir Harold Wernher, Bt.

209   **Chelsea Porcelain: Huntsman and Lady (A Pair)**
H. 10½ in., *c.* 1765.   Mark: gold anchor.
Lent by Sir Harold Wernher, Bt.

210   **Mahogany Tripod Tea Table**
H. 30 in., Diam. 29½ in., *c.* 1755.   Serpentine top and spindle gallery; shaft spirally fluted, cabriole legs carved with rococo ornament; paw-feet. Lit: *D.E.F.*, III, p. 206, fig. 12.
Lent by Ralph Edwards, Esq.

211   **Silver-gilt Cup and Cover and Salver**
H. (Cup) 14½ in.   Diam. (Salver) 15¼ in.   By Gabriel Sleath, 1740. Coll: intended as a present from the Irish Society to Henry Singleton, Lord Chief Justice of the Common Pleas in Ireland; on being declined, added by the Society to the Mansion House Plate.   Exh: Goldsmiths' Hall, *Corporation Plate of England and Wales*, 1952, No. 133.   Bell-shaped body richly embossed with rococo ornament, shaped handles and domed cover; round tray with cast border decorated with masks.
Lent by the Corporation of London.

212   **Silver Table and Stand**
H. 25½, Diam. 21½ in.   Maker's mark: *E.C., c.* 1760.   Octagonal top, pierced border; baluster stem with lion masks, tripod base; with coat of arms and rococo ornament.
Lent by Mrs. David Gubbay.

213 Mahogany Tripod Table

H. 28 in. Diam. 27 in., *c.* 1755. Edge of top carved and pierced with scrolls and foliage; shaft with acanthus decoration; legs formed of double scrolls.
Lent by Mrs. Geoffrey Hart.

214 Queen Charlotte's Jewel Cabinet

$43 \times 32\frac{1}{2} \times 22$ in. By Vile and Cobb for Queen Charlotte, 1761. Mahogany, rococo ornament, veneered in various woods; doors and top inlaid with ivory, interior fitted with small drawers; supported on cabriole legs with scroll feet. Coll: Marquess of Cambridge. Lit: H. Clifford Smith, *Buckingham Palace*, London 1931, pp. 73–4. *D.E.F.*, I, p. 186, figs. 44, 45: pp. 154–5.
Lent by Her Majesty The Queen (Windsor Castle).

215 Pair of Silver-gilt Tea Caddies

H. $9\frac{3}{4}$ in. By John Payne, 1769. Pear-shaped, embossed with floral ornament; with arms of the Company.
Lent by the Worshipful Company of Goldsmiths.

LOUIS FRANÇOIS ROUBILIAC (1702/5–1762)

216 George II

Marble bust. H. 31 in. Signed: *L. F. Roubiliac Inv$^{t\cdot}$* Lit: K. A. Esdaile, *Louis François Roubiliac*, London 1928, p. 91, Pl. XXXVa.
Lent by Her Majesty The Queen (Windsor Castle).

217 Pair of Brackets

H. 21 in., *c.* 1775. Eagles with C-scrolls and pierced rococo foliage supporting shelves.
Lent by Mrs. David Gubbay.

218 Mirror in Gilt Circular Frame

57×52 in., *c.* 1750. Circle formed of oak leaves, candle branches repeating motif; sun rays from central head of Apollo. Lit: *D.E.F.*, II, p. 343, fig. 84: p. 345.
Lent by Sir Charles Chute, Bt.

219 Mahogany Armchair

$42\frac{1}{4} \times 25\frac{1}{2} \times 20\frac{1}{2}$ in., *c.* 1755. Cresting centring in shell cabochon and acanthus foliage; arms and legs formed of dolphins; seat-rail and shoulders of legs carved with foliated ornament. Back, seat and

arms covered in needlework of later date.   Lit: P. MacQuoid, *English Furniture . . . in the Lady Lever Art Gallery*, London 1928, No. 148, Pl. 45 (as No. 146).   *D.E.F.*, I, p. 278, fig. 161: p. 276.
Lent by the Lady Lever Art Gallery.

220   Mahogany Pole-screen

H. 65½ in., *c.* 1760.   Tripod with cabriole legs, ending in volutes, carved with foliage; fluted shaft; panel probably Beauvais tapestry.
Lent by the Shaftesbury Estates Company.

In Gallery IX

221   Clock and Pedestal

H. 91 in.   By Charles Clay, *c.* 1735–40.   Signed: *Being the first/made in perfection/N: 1 Cha: Clay London Fect*.   Face with ormolu relief and background painted with mythological scene in oil; back and sides, ormolu chased and pierced with masks, foliage and trophies; domed case and pedestal veneered with ebony, ormolu and brass mounts; musical accompaniment.   Lit: E. Croft Murray, "Musical Clocks by Charles Clay," *Country Life*, CVII, 1950, pp. 1112–14.
Lent by Major-General Lord Burnham.

GALLERY VII

CHINOISERIE

222   Chinese Wallpaper

Eight pieces, each approx. 122 × 45 in. Mid-XVIIIth Century.
From a set of twelve pieces formerly at Avebury Manor.
Lent by Messrs. Pratt and Sons, Ltd.

223   Pair of Japanned Chairs

41 × 20 × 19 in., *c.* 1718. Caned backs with vase-shaped splats
japanned in green and gold with oriental motifs, apron centring in
shell, legs carved with shell and husk; claw-and-ball feet.   Lit: P.
MacQuoid, *English Furniture . . . in the Lady Lever Art Gallery*,
London 1928, No. 182, Pl. 52.
Lent by the Lady Lever Art Gallery.

224   Mahogany Armchair, in Chinese Taste

53 × 29 × 20½ in., *c.* 1755.   Back, arms and wings filled with lattice-
work; cresting of acanthus decoration; covered in contemporary
needlework.
Lent by Mrs. David Gubbay.

225   Lacquered Work-box on Stand

37 × 15 × 11 in., *c.* 1755.   Gilt stand carved with rococo ornament.
Lit: *D.E.F.*, I, p. 111, fig. 28.
Lent by the Earl of Radnor.

226   Soho Chinoiserie Tapestry: The Harpist

Silk and wool on woollen warp.   109 × 113 in.   Early XVIIIth Century.
Exh: Birmingham, *English Tapestries*, 1951, No. 41b.
Lent by the Earl of Leven and Melville.

227   Pair of Mahogany Settees, in Chinese Taste

36½ × 45 × 22 in., *c.* 1760.   Backs and arms pierced and carved with
pagodas, arcading and lattice-work; covered in contemporary needlework.
Lent by Mrs. David Gubbay.

70

228 Mahogany Centre Table, in Chinese Taste

29 × 31½ × 21½ in., *c.* 1760. Pierced fretwork gallery, apron and stretcher; cluster column legs.
Lent by A. Wyndham Green, Esq.

229 Tea-caddy

H. 9½ in., *c.* 1775. Rosewood banded with kingwood and inlaid with musical instruments and chinoiserie figures; a brass finial in the form of a classic urn.
Lent by M. Moore, Esq.

230 Mirror, with Frame in Chinese Taste

94 × 48 in., *c.* 1760. Carved frame japanned and parcel-gilt; under canopy on the cresting a grotesque ape. Lit: *D.E.F.*, II, p. 343, fig. 85: p. 341.
Lent by the Earl Fitzwilliam.

231 Pair of Mahogany Stools, in Chinese Taste

21 × 36 × 15 in., *c.* 1755. Seat-rails decorated with fretwork; cluster column legs and double stretchers; covered in contemporary Italian velvet.
Lent by the Duke of Bedford.

232 Pair of Japanned Armchairs, in Chinese Taste

36½ × 25 × 18 in., *c.* 1760. Arms and backs filled with lattice-work; japanned in black with gold flower designs; damask covers of later date.
Lent by the Hon. Mrs. Ionides.

233 Soho Chinoiserie Tapestry

Silk and wool on woollen warp. 93 × 80 in. Early XVIIIth Century. By M. Mazarind. Coll: from a series of five pieces said to have been bought by the Empress Catherine of Russia from Houghton. Lit: H. C. Marillier, *English Tapestries of the Eighteenth Century*, London 1930, pp. 34, 35.
Lent by Christabel, Lady Aberconway.

RICHARD WILSON, R.A. (1713–1782)

234 The Pagoda at Kew

Canvas. 19 × 29½ in. Exh: Society of Artists, 1762, No. 131. Lit: W. G. Constable, *Richard Wilson*, London 1953, pp. 179–80,

Pl. 41B. Horace Walpole mentions without enthusiasm Chinese buildings at Wroxton in 1753 as the first of their kind (John Summerson, *Architecture in Great Britain*, London 1953, p. 220). They were probably taken from William Halfpenny's *Rural Architecture in the Chinese Taste*, 2nd Ed., 1750–52 (see No. 280) with designs which are as much French rococo as Chinese and were probably concocted from French prints. Sir William Chambers was employed at Kew by Augusta, Dowager Princess of Wales, from 1757–62, and during this time the Pagoda, the first important architectural work in the Chinese taste, was built. It was not generally admired and Chambers did not persist with the style. Such "curiosities", incongruous in an architect who defended Roman as the only fit style, he regarded as permissible for variety and novelty. In 1757 he had published his *Designs of Chinese Buildings*, the first account in England to provide authentic evidence of the subject (see No. 279). A further chinoiserie building by Chambers was the temple for the Duchess of Queensberry at Amesbury, Wiltshire, in 1772. Walpole objected to Chambers' "unmeaning falballas of Chinese Chequer work". He referred more than once to the Pagoda at Kew. In a letter to Lord Strafford, 5th July 1761, he writes: "We begin to perceive the tower at Kew from Montpellier Row: in a fortnight you will see it in Yorkshire."
Lent by Mrs. Geoffrey Hart.

235 Standing Shelves, in Chinese Taste

$79 \times 56 \times 20$ in., *c.* 1755. Japanned; shelves with fretwork galleries surmounted by pagoda canopies; panels filled with lattice-work. Exh: *B.F.A.C.*, Winter 1935, No. 23. Lit: *D.E.F.*, III, pp. 117–18, fig. 5.
Lent by Viscount Scarsdale.

236 Mirror, with Carved and Gilt Frame, in Chinese Taste

70×44 in., *c.* 1755. Branches at sides support brackets for porcelain; on cresting beneath pagoda with bells, male Chinese figure; flanked by stylised birds.
Lent by the Hon. Mrs. Reginald Fellowes.

237 Soho Chinoiserie Tapestry: The Procession of the Emperor

Silk and wool on woollen warp. 108×152 in. Early XVIIIth Century. Exh: Birmingham, *English Tapestries*, 1951, No. 41a.
Lent by the Earl of Leven and Melville.

238 **Mahogany Breakfast Table, in Chinese Taste**

30 × 25 × 22 in., *c.* 1765. Based on a design in Chippendale's *Director*, 1st Edn., 1754, Pl. XXXIII. Taper legs, folding flaps, back and sides filled with lattice-work; sunk panels on supports carved with trefoils; shaped shelf.
Lent by Ralph Edwards, Esq.

239 **Table Clock in Japanned Case**

H. 29 in. By Joseph Antram (inscribed), *c.* 1750–60. Japanned green with gold decoration; terminal figures at corners, brass finials on hood; movement with musical chime and eight tunes.
Lent by Lord Kenyon.

240 **Mahogany Settee, in Chinese Taste**

39 × 60 × 22 in., *c.* 1755. Double chair form; arms and back with pagoda crestings filled with lattice-work; cover of later date.
Lent by C. D. Rotch, Esq.

241 **Pair of Japanned Standing Shelves**

58¾ × 22½ × 10½ in., *c.* 1755. Three tiers, japanned in red, black and gold; pagoda-roofed tops supported by twisted columns; two lower compartments with lattice-work sides in Chinese taste. Coll: Badminton. Lit: P. MacQuoid, *English Furniture . . . in the Lady Lever Art Gallery*, London 1928, No. 168, Pl. 52.
Lent by the Lady Lever Art Gallery.

242 **Bow Porcelain: A Mandarin**

H. 9 in., *c.* 1755. Unmarked: probably from Meissen original. Pair to No. 251.
Lent by Sir Kenneth Clark.

243 **Worcester Porcelain: Two Plates, Tea Cup and Saucer, Coffee Cup and Saucer, Two-Handled Cup and Saucer**

c. 1770 (Dr. Wall period).
Lent by A. Wyndham Green, Esq.

244 **Pair of Mirrors in Carved and Gilt Frames, in Chinese Taste**

104 × 58 in. Based on a design in the 1st Edition of Chippendale's *Director*, 1754, Pl. CXLIII. Differs from the design in that here a Chinese youth and not a mandarin is placed on the cresting under the pagoda canopy. Lit: *D.E.F.*, II, pp. 341–2, fig. 79.
Lent by the Hon. Mrs. George Marten.

245 **Commode, Lacquered and Japanned in Chinese Taste**

38 × 48 × 25 in., *c.* 1765. Serpentine front; top and three drawers veneered with oriental lacquer, the decoration of the drawers forming a continuous design in black and gold in low relief; sides and borders of English japan; hoof feet; escutcheons and handles gilt-brass. Lit: *D.E.F.*, II, p. 114, fig. 12; p. 110.
Lent by the Shaftesbury Estates Company.

246 **Pair of Mahogany Armchairs, in Chinese Taste**

39 × 27 × 21 in., *c.* 1755. Backs and sides filled with lattice-work; legs carved with frets; silk covers of later date.
Lent by A. Wyndham Green, Esq.

247 **Wall-clock in Carved and Gilt Frame**

H. 41 in., *c.* 1755. Softwood, gilt; pierced and carved with scrollwork surmounted by pagoda; a fox at the bottom regarding a bunch of grapes. (The dial, not original to the clock, signed: *James Gibbs, London.*) Lit: P. MacQuoid, *English Furniture . . . in the Lady Lever Art Gallery*, London 1928, No. 450, Pl. 99.
Lent by the Lady Lever Art Gallery.

248 **Cabinet and Stand, in Chinese Taste**

102½ × 77 × 21 in., *c.* 1755. Centre compartment surmounted by pagoda roof, with escutcheon and two bracket candlesticks; lattice-work gallery with corner vases; stand decorated with card-cut lattice-work and scroll brackets; doors veneered with amboyna wood; the hundred drawers in interior veneered with a large variety of coloured woods. Lit: *D.E.F.*, I, p. 182, fig. 35; Pl. V, p. 181.
Lent by Viscount Leverhulme.

249 **Stool, in Chinese Taste**

17 × 19 × 19 in., *c.* 1755. One of a pair; legs, seat-rail and stretcher carved with fretwork; covered in contemporary needlework.
Lent by Mrs. David Gubbay.

250 **Commode, Lacquered and Japanned in Chinese Taste**

37 × 52 × 27 in., *c.* 1765. Top and doors veneered with panels of oriental lacquer; borders of English japan; ormolu mounts on cabriole; corners show neo-classic influence.
Lent by the National Trust (Polesden Lacey).

251 **Bow Porcelain: A Mandarin's Wife.**

H. 9 in., c. 1755. Unmarked: probably from Meissen original. Pair
to No. 242.
Lent by Sir Kenneth Clark.

252 **Soho Chinoiserie Tapestry**

Silk and wool on woollen warp. 92 × 153 in. Early XVIIIth Century.
Signed: *M. Mazarind* (with the mark of white shield bearing red cross).
Coll: from a series of five pieces said to have been bought by the
Empress Catherine of Russia from Houghton. Lit: H. C. Marillier,
English Tapestries of the Eighteenth Century, London 1930, pp. 34, 35.
Lent by Christabel, Lady Aberconway.

253 **Pair of Mahogany Chairs, in Chinese Taste**

39½ × 23 × 19 in., c. 1755. Top rails carved with pagoda ornament;
splat with lattice-work; uprights and seat-rails with frets; cluster
column legs; silk covers of later date.
Lent by C. D. Rotch, Esq.

254 **Mahogany Cabinet on Stand**

41 × 26 × 13 in., c. 1755. Stand carved with fretwork in Chinese
taste; cluster column legs.
Lent by Mrs. David Gubbay.

255 **Pair of Pier-tables**

37½ × 65 × 20½ in. Designed by Henry Holland for the Prince of
Wales's Chinese Drawing-room at Carlton House; probably made by
Robert Campbell, upholsterer and cabinet-maker to the Prince,
c. 1790. Ebony veneer, *rosso antico* tops and ormolu mounts; bronze
terminal figures of Chinamen. Lit: H. Clifford Smith, *Buckingham
Palace*, London 1931, p. 221, Pl. 271. *D.E.F.*, III, p. 300, fig. 76:
pp. 299, 303.
Lent by Her Majesty The Queen (Buckingham Palace).

256 **Silver Tea-kettle and Stand**

H. 18 in. Makers' mark: *CW, TW, 1761.* Pear-shaped; decorated
with Chinese figures, pagodas and rococo cartouches and scrolling.
Lent by the Hon. Mrs. Ionides.

257 **Needlework Panel, in Chinese Taste**

37½ × 66½ in., c. 1750. Decorated with landscape and figures.
Lent by Mrs. David Gubbay.

SIR JOSHUA REYNOLDS, P.R.A. (1723–1792)

258 Wang-y-Tong

Canvas. 50 × 40 in. Lit: E. K. Waterhouse, *Reynolds*, London 1941, p. 67, Pl. 167. Painted *c.* 1776 (Waterhouse). There is, of course, nothing chinoiserie about this painting. Indeed Reynolds, the champion of the Grand Manner, who exhorted his students to imbibe the works of Michelangelo and Raphael, would have been the last man to seek inspiration from lacquer screens and K'ang-hsi vases. It is included because it represents a Chinese boy seated on what appears to be a chinoiserie settee, and because it reflects the eighteenth-century taste for everything Chinese although, as it is pointed out in the Introduction, Chinoiserie was on the wane and neo-classicism in the ascendant when this picture was painted. The sitter was a Chinese page in the service of the Duchess of Dorset at Knole, and sent by her to be educated at Sevenoaks School.

Lent by Lord Sackville.

259 **Mahogany Cabinet on Stand, in Chinese Taste**

76 × 28 × 15 in., *c.* 1760. Canopy with pagoda top supported on lattice-work; panels veneered with wood varnished and stained to simulate lacquer and ornamented with oriental soapstone carving.

Lent by Mrs. David Gubbay.

260 **Silver Tray**

Diam. 25 in. By William Cripps, 1758. Circular; cast openwork border with figures of Chinese musicians and birds; rococo scrolling; centre with arms of Douglas in rococo cartouche.

Lent by the Hon. Mrs. Ionides.

261 **Silver Tea-urn**

H. 21½ in. No marks, *c.* 1760. Pear-shaped with Chinese figure with sunshade on knop of lid; figures of musicians and fishermen, rococo scrolling and cartouches on body; square base.

Lent by the Hon. Mrs. Ionides.

262 **Soho Chinoiserie Tapestry**

Silk and wool on woollen warp. 93 × 144 in. Early XVIIIth Century. Signed: *J. Vanderbanc, In Great Queen* (Street). Exh: Birmingham, *English Tapestries*, 1951, No. 42. Lit: H. C. Marillier, *English Tapestries of the Eighteenth Century*, London 1930, p. 33.

Lent by the Earl of Bradford.

263   Dressing-table, in Chinese Taste

72 × 40 × 24 in., *c.* 1770. Veneered with satinwood, kingwood, mahogany and other woods; pagoda crestings; adjustable mirror; drawer in frieze fitted for dressing; cupboards and top inlaid with chinoiserie figures. A late example of the Chinese style. (The brass handles in neo-classic taste.)
Lent by Mrs. David Gubbay.

264   Mahogany Chair, in Chinese Taste

39½ × 23 × 19 in., *c.* 1755. Cresting centring in pagoda, back of lattice-work ornamented with rosettes; legs and uprights with fretwork; covered in contemporary needlework.
Lent by Mrs. David Gubbay.

265   Standing Shelves, in Chinese Taste

61¼ × 23 × 11 in., *c.* 1755. Three tiers, japanned black, with gold decoration; pagoda top with bells at corners, centre compartment with doors, lower with lattice-work sides. Exh: *B.F.A.C.*, Winter 1935, No. 34a; Belgrave Hall, Leicester (on loan).
Lent by Alice, Countess of Gainsborough.

ARCHITECTURAL ROOM
GOTHIC

ENGLISH SCHOOL

266 Sanderson Miller

Canvas. 30×25 in.   Reputed to be a portrait of Sanderson Miller (1717–80), an amateur architect who practised mainly in the gothic style.   In the 40's he built two gothic follies which had the distinction of being amongst the first of their kind and in the 50's he shared with Horace Walpole the reputation of being an acknowledged authority on all things gothic.   He was consulted by friends anxious to embellish their parks and designed gothic follies at Hagley, Wimpole, Prior Park and elsewhere.   At Lacock Abbey he was allowed to gothicise the house itself.   In London he was responsible for a gothic house for the Countess of Pomfret in Arlington Street, 1760.   One of the gothic picture-frames from this house is No. 270 (see H. M. Colvin, *Dictionary of English Architects*, 1954, pp. 388–9).
Lent by the National Trust (Lacock Abbey).

267 Pair of Mahogany Chairs, in Gothic Taste

$39 \times 25 \times 25$ in., *c.* 1760.   From a set including a settee; seat-rail carved with gothic arches and trefoil ornament; legs and stretchers carved and pierced with quatrefoils.   Embroidery covers worked by Lady Newdigate, mother of Sir Roger, who "gothicised" Arbury.
Lent by F. H. M. Fitzroy-Newdegate, Esq.

268 Knee-hole Writing-table, in Gothic Taste

$36 \times 52 \times 24$ in., *c.* 1755.   Frieze and cupboards carved with gothic arcading and ornament; cupboards flanked by cluster columns. This table closely follows a design for a "Gothic Writing Table" in Chippendale's *Director* (1st Edn., 1754, Pl. LII; 3rd Edn., 1762, Pl. LXXVI).   In a similar table (see *D.E.F.*, III, p. 248, fig. 119) plain cabriole legs are substituted for those of pillar form, which in the present table follow the design.
Lent by the Hon. Mrs. Reginald Fellowes.

269 Brass Inkstand, in Gothic Taste
H. $6\frac{1}{2}$ in., *c.* 1750–60.
Lent by the Hon. Mrs. Reginald Fellowes.

GOTHIC

THOMAS BARDWELL (d. c. 1780)

270 The Earl and Countess of Pomfret

Canvas. 85 × 49 in. Presented to the Ashmolean Museum by the Countess of Pomfret, 1759. Lit: Mrs. Poole, *Catalogue of Oxford Portraits*, Oxford 1912, Vol. I, p. 188, No. 456. This picture is exhibited on account of its gothic frame which was designed for the gothic drawing-room of the Pomfrets' house in Arlington Street, which was built by Sanderson Miller (see No. 266) in 1760. There appear to have been two gothic houses in Arlington Street as No. 17 was built for the Hon. Henry Pelham in the gothic style between 1741 and 1750. It was begun by William Kent and completed after his death in 1748 by Stephen Wright. Horace Walpole lived in Arlington Street and, describing a tempest in 1779, wrote: "One of the stone Gothic towers at Lady Pomfret's house (now single-speech Hamilton's) in my street fell through the roof, and not a thought of it remains." Thomas Fermor (1698–1753), 2nd Baron Leominster, was created Earl of Pomfret in 1721; in 1727 he was appointed Master of the Horse to Queen Caroline. He married Henrietta Louisa, daughter of the 2nd Lord Jeffreys, in 1720. After the death of her husband she bought from her son his statues, which had formed part of the Arundel collection and had been purchased by his grandfather, and presented them to Oxford University. She died in 1761. *Lent by the Ashmolean Museum, Oxford.*

SIR WILLIAM BEECHEY, R.A. (1753–1839)

271 James Wyatt, P.R.A.

Canvas. 26½ × 21½ in. Exh: R.A. Winter 1934 (342). James Wyatt (1746–1813) became Surveyor-General to the Board of Works, 1796, and President of the Royal Academy for one year in 1805. H. M. Colvin (*Dictionary of English Architects*, 1954, pp. 722–32) points out that the real importance of Wyatt's gothic work "lay in the manner in which it bridged the gap between the rococo gothic of the mid-eighteenth century and the serious medievalism of the early nineteenth." Fonthill Abbey, Wiltshire, built by Wyatt for William Beckford, 1796–1807, was one of the landmarks of the Gothic Revival in England. Amongst Wyatt's gothic country houses was Lee Priory, Kent, built for Thomas Barrett, 1783–90. The Glazed Door (No. 292) and the Painted Wood Stoup (No. 289) both come from this house, which was demolished in 1953. *Lent by the Royal Academy of Arts.*

272 **Clock in Mahogany Case, in Gothic Taste**

H. 25¼ in., *c.* 1795. Gothic arched top, flanked by finials; inlaid with brass.
Lent by the Hon. Rowland Winn.

273 **Bedside Cupboard**

31 × 24½ × 18½ in., *c.* 1755–60. Doors carved with gothic tracery; gallery top.
Lent by the Hon. Mrs. Reginald Fellowes.

274 **Armchair, in Gothic Taste**

38½ × 19 × 18 in., *c.* 1760. One of a set painted black and gold; two quatrefoils below cusped arches on back. Lit: *D.E.F.*, I, p. 283, fig. 182.
Lent by the Hon. Sherman Stonor.

275 **Mahogany Bookcase, in Gothic Taste**

112 × 133 × 16 in., *c.* 1785. Break-front section shallower than flanking wings; gallery of central section pierced with arcade of trefoil-headed arches, those above wings with quatrefoils; pointed finials at corners; glazing bars of gothic tracery; lower stage carved with arcading and a cross motif.
Lent by Ian L. Phillips, Esq.

276 **Vitruvius Britannicus or The British Architect by Colen Campbell (London 1725)**

Folio, 2 vols. in one, 100 plates, bound leather. The work was published in 5 vols., 1715–71.
Lent by the Royal Academy of Arts.

277 **The Analysis of Beauty by William Hogarth (London 1772)**

Quarto, 2 plates and frontispiece, bound leather. The first edition was published in 1753.
Lent by the Royal Academy of Arts.

278 **The Designs of Inigo Jones by William Kent (London, Benjamin White, 1770)**

Folio, 2 vols. in one, 138 plates and 2 frontispieces, quarter bound leather. The work was first published in 1727.
Lent by the Royal Academy of Arts.

279 Designs of Chinese Buildings, etc., by Sir William Chambers, R.A. (London 1757)

Folio, 2 vols. in one, 43 plates, bound leather. Full title: *Designs of Chinese Buildings, Furniture, Dresses, Machines, and Utensils, engraved by the Best Hands, from the Originals drawn in China by Mr. Chambers, Architect.*
Lent by the Royal Academy of Arts.

280 Rural Architecture in the Chinese Taste by William and John Halfpenny (London, Robert Sayer, 1752)

Second edition, octavo, in four parts, engraved frontispiece and 60 plates, in original calf binding. Full title: *Rural Architecture in the Chinese Taste, Being Designs Entirely New for the Decoration of Gardens, Parks, Forrests, Insides of Houses, & etc., on Sixty Copper Plates with full Instructions for Workmen ALSO a near Estimate of the Charge and Hints where proper to be Erected.*
Lent by Francis Stonor, Esq.

281 The Gardens and Buildings at Kew by Sir William Chambers, R.A. (London, J. Haberkorn, 1763)

Folio, 35 plates, bound in contemporary half calf. Full title: *Plans Elevations, Sections, and Perspective Views of the Gardens and Buildings at Kew in Surrey, The seat of Her Royal Highness The Princess Dowager of Wales.*
Lent by Francis Stonor, Esq.

282 A Description of the Villa of Horace Walpole at Strawberry Hill, near Twickenham (Strawberry Hill, Thomas Kirgate, 1774)

Small quarto, frontispiece, quarter bound leather.
Lent by the Royal Academy of Arts.

283 The Gentleman and Cabinet-Maker's Director by Thomas Chippendale (London 1754)

Folio, 160 plates, bound leather.
Lent by the Royal Academy of Arts.

284 The Ruins of Palmyra otherwise Tedmor in the Desart by Robert Wood (London 1753)

Folio, 57 plates, bound vellum, gilt tooled.
Lent by the Royal Academy of Arts.

285 **Catalogo degli Antichi Monumenti di Ercolano by Ottavio Antonio Bayardi (Naples 1755–92)**

Folio, one of 8 vols., bound leather.
Lent by the Royal Academy of Arts.

286 **Ruins of the Palace of the Emperor Diocletian at Spalatro in Dalmatia by Robert Adam (London 1764)**

Folio, 61 plates and frontispiece, bound in red leather, gilt tooled. Inscribed: *"Mr. Adam presents his Compliments to Mr. Chambers & sends him a copy of the Ruins of Diocletians Palace at Spalatro which he begs Mr. Chambers will do him the Honour to present to the Royal Academy & Beg their Acceptance of it, and of his sincere wishes for the prosperity of so great & so usefull an Institution."*
Lent by the Royal Academy of Arts.

287 **The Discourses of Sir Joshua Reynolds, P.R.A., with an Account of the Life and Writings of the Author by Edmond Malone (London 1797)**

Quarto, one of 2 vols. containing other writings by Reynolds, frontispiece, bound leather, gilt tooling.
Lent by the Royal Academy of Arts.

288 **The Antiquities of Athens by James Stuart and Nicholas Revett (London, John Haberkorn, 1762)**

Folio, the first of 4 vols., 70 plates and frontispiece, bound in leather, gilt tooled.
Lent by the Royal Academy of Arts.

289 **Painted Wood Stoup**

36 × 15 × 8 in., *c.* 1782. Gothic arch; white, with red and blue decoration; base decorated with rosettes on corbel support. Coll: Lee Priory, Kent. (See No. 292.)
Lent by Ian L. Phillips, Esq.

290 **Jardinière, in Gothic Taste**

29½ × 27 × 20 in., *c.* 1755. Oak, carved with gothic arcades and motifs; turned supports with octagonal finials.
Lent by the Hon. Mrs. Reginald Fellowes.

SPIRIDONE ROMA (d. 1787)

291 Gothic Decorations for the Chapel at The Vyne

Distemper on canvas. 116×426 in. Signed: *Spir . . . oni Roma.*
Decorations for the Chapel at The Vyne, Hampshire, executed *c.* 1770,
formerly on walls above stalls, now in the Gallery. The counterfeited
fan vaulting is modelled on Gloucester Cathedral. The oil sketch by
Roma, showing his original project, is at The Vyne. Roma, born in
Corfu, came to England *c.* 1770 and was employed by John Chute at
The Vyne. On being dismissed for idleness he set up as a picture
restorer, gaining considerable practice among the City Companies. He
remained in England until his death in 1787. (The information on
Roma has been kindly supplied by Mr. Edward Croft Murray, whose
Decorative Painting in England 1537–1837 is to be published by
Country Life.)
Lent by Sir Charles Chute, Bt.

292 Glazed Door

92 × 46 in., *c.* 1782. Removed from Lee Priory, Kent (built by James
Wyatt in gothic taste, 1783–90, and demolished in 1953). Painted
white with red and blue decoration; Perpendicular style with coloured
glass in tracery; lower stage with gothic arcading and leaf decoration
above and in spandrels.
Lent by Ian L. Phillips, Esq.

293 Mahogany Settee, in Gothic Taste

42 × 64 × 22 in., *c.* 1755–60. Back and arms filled with gothic
arcading; seat-rail fluted; front supports and pierced brackets carved
with gothic motifs.
Lent by the Hon. Mrs. Reginald Fellowes.

294 Mahogany Armchair, in Gothic Taste

44½ × 27½ × 21 in., *c.* 1750–55. Back and arms with gothic arcading;
front supports of cluster columns.
Lent by the Hon. Mrs. Reginald Fellowes.

295 Mahogany Armchair, in Gothic Taste

66 × 28 × 20 in., *c.* 1750. From the Chapel at Audley End. Back and
sides filled with gothic tracery; uprights and crestings with finials;
arms end in child-headed supports carved with foliage.
Lent by the Ministry of Works (Audley End).

296 Mahogany Chair, in Gothic Taste

$46 \times 23 \times 19\frac{1}{2}$ in., *c.* 1750. Back filled with gothic tracery; uprights surmounted by finials.

Lent by the Hon. Mrs. Reginald Fellowes.

297 Mahogany Settee, in Gothic Taste

$38\frac{1}{2} \times 72 \times 23$ in., *c.* 1750. Back and arms filled with interlaced arcading; top rail carved with acanthus foliage; needlework of later date.

Lent by the Duke of Bedford.

298 Mahogany Lectern, in Gothic Taste

$59 \times 35 \times 48$ in., *c.* 1750. Carved with gothic tracery. From the Chapel at Audley End.

Lent by the Ministry of Works (Audley End).

299 Mirror, in Gothic Taste

81×33 in. Designed by Horace Walpole for Strawberry Hill, *c.* 1755. Carved and decorated in black and gold; with portrait of George Walpole, 3rd Earl of Orford.

Lent by Lord Walpole.

300 Pair of Carved and Gilt Panel-decorations

H. 67 in., *c.* 1760. Carved with open-work gothic tracery, oak trees and scrolls and foliage. Lit: P. MacQuoid, *English Furniture . . . in the Lady Lever Art Gallery*, London 1928, No. 112, Pl. 34.

Lent by the Lady Lever Art Gallery.

301 Pair of Painted Chairs, in Gothic Taste

$39 \times 20 \times 18$ in., *c.* 1750–55. Backs filled with arcading and quatrefoils; cluster column legs. From the Chapel at Audley End.

Lent by the Ministry of Works (Audley End).

302 Mirror, in Gothic Taste

90×50 in., *c.* 1755. Carved and decorated in black and gold. En suite with Console Table, No. 303.

Lent by Sir Charles Chute, Bt.

303 Console Table, in Gothic Taste

$33 \times 55 \times 22$ in., *c.* 1755. Carved and decorated in black and gold; cluster column legs, apron of gothic arcading. En suite with Mirror, No. 302.

Lent by Sir Charles Chute, Bt.

304   Bureau Clock in Brass Case, in Gothic Taste
H. 8 in., *c.* 1750–60.
Lent by the Hon. Mrs. Reginald Fellowes.

ARTHUR DEVIS (1708–1787)

305   Sir Roger Newdigate in his Gothic Library

Canvas.   35 × 30 in.   Lit: S. H. Paviere, *The Devis Family of Painters*, Leigh-on-Sea 1950, p. 52, No. 110.   Sir Roger Newdigate (1719–1806), 5th Bt., M.P. for the University of Oxford, a high Tory whom Horace Walpole referred to as "a half-converted Jacobite"; a collector of ancient marbles and the founder of the Newdigate prize at Oxford.   It was he who rebuilt Arbury in the gothic style.   The remodelling of the library in that style was carried out by William Hiorn from *c.* 1750 onwards.   The gothicising of the house was not completed until *c.* 1790 (see H. M. Colvin, *Dictionary of English Architects*, 1954, pp. 281, 336).
Lent by F. H. M. Fitzroy-Newdegate, Esq.

306   Armchair, in Gothic Taste

39 × 22 × 19 in., *c.* 1765.   One of a set.   Softwood painted green and gold.   Lit: *D.E.F.*, I, p. 283, fig. 182.
Lent by the Hon. Sherman Stonor.

307   Pair of Chairs, in Gothic Taste

38 × 23 × 18 in., *c.* 1755–60.   Backs formed of arcades of cusped tracery; uprights and front legs of cluster-columns.
Lent by the Hon. Mrs. Reginald Fellowes.

308   Mahogany Side-table, in Gothic Taste

$32\frac{3}{4}$ × $49\frac{1}{2}$ × $25\frac{1}{4}$ in., *c.* 1760.   One of a pair; frieze arcaded in low relief, undulating in convex and concave curves; hexagonal legs decorated with frets; pierced angle brackets; Convent-Siena marble top carved with satyr masks.   Lit: P. MacQuoid, *English Furniture . . . in the Lady Lever Art Gallery*, London 1928, No. 234, Pl. 62.
Lent by the Lady Lever Art Gallery.

309   South Front of Strawberry Hill

Aquatint by F. Jukes, 1784, after E. Edwards, A.R.A.
Lent by St. Mary's College, Strawberry Hill.

310 View from the Great Bedchamber at Strawberry Hill

Engraving (coloured) by Godfrey after Pars.

Lent by St. Mary's College, Strawberry Hill.

311 The Gallery at Strawberry Hill

Engraving (coloured) by J. C. Stadler.

Lent by St. Mary's College, Strawberry Hill.

312 Entrance of Strawberry Hill

Engraving (coloured) by J. Newton after E. Edwards, A.R.A.

Lent by St. Mary's College, Strawberry Hill.

J. G. ECCARDT (d. 1779)

313 Horace Walpole

Canvas. $15\frac{1}{2} \times 12\frac{1}{2}$ in. An old manuscript label on the back of the stretcher reads: *Horace Walpole youngest son of Sir R. Walpole by Eckardt 1754.* Coll: from Strawberry Hill, Lot 28 of the 22nd day's sale, 1842. Engr: Anon. 1798. In Walpole's description of Strawberry Hill (*Works*, 1798, II, 436) this picture is described as "Mr. Horace Walpole; from Vandyck, leaning on the Aedes Walpolianae; behind him a view of Strawberry Hill". The *Aedes Walpolianae* is his description of his father's—the Prime Minister's—house and collection at Houghton. Horace Walpole started turning Strawberry Hill into a gothic villa in about 1750. Although it cannot be claimed that he was the pioneer, Horace Walpole became the champion and accepted authority on the "Gothic Revival" (see the Introduction). In this room will be seen the gothic looking-glass designed by him for Strawberry Hill (No. 299). The gothic console table and looking-glass (Nos. 302 and 303) and the gothic wall decorations (No. 291) from The Vyne belonged to his friend John Chute (1701–76), one of the "Committee of Taste", at whose death Walpole wrote that he was "my oracle in Taste, the standard to whom I submitted my Trifles, and the genius that presided over poor Strawberry!" The Devis painting (No. 305) shows Sir Roger Newdigate, an admirer of Walpole, in his library, the bookcases of which were designed in the Strawberry Hill manner.

Lent by the National Portrait Gallery.

314 Strawberry Hill

Engraving (coloured) by E. Rooker after Paul Sandby, R.A., published by G. Keandy, 1774.

Lent by St. Mary's College, Strawberry Hill.

315 **South Front of Strawberry Hill, with view of the Thames**

Aquatint by J. C. Stadler after J. Farington, R.A., published by J. Boydell, 1793.

Lent by St. Mary's College, Strawberry Hill.

EDWARD EDWARDS, A.R.A. (1738–1806)

316 **North Front of Strawberry Hill**

Water-colour. $11\frac{1}{2} \times 10$ in. Signed and dated: *E.E. 1783*. Presented to the College by Mr. W. S. Lewis.

Lent by St. Mary's College, Strawberry Hill.

LECTURE ROOM
NEO-CLASSIC

317 Pair of Oyster-spa Urns

H. 24 in., *c.* 1780.   Pierced and chased ormolu mounts; pomegranate knops, rams' head handles; neo-classic scroll design on rims, wreaths of bay leaves at bases.
Lent by Capt. J. B. E. Radcliffe.

318 Pier-glass in Carved and Gilt Frame

108 × 43 in., *c.* 1775–80.   Surmounted by urn and acanthus foliage; side pilasters with holly-leaf decoration and urn finials.
Lent by the Earl of Onslow.

319 Pair of Painted Candlestands

H. 66 in.   Probably designed by James Wyatt, *c.* 1795.   Tripods carved with female terminals, supporting metal candle branches; single column with twisted serpents from each bowl; the decoration renewed after a fire at Heveningham.   Lit: *D.E.F.*, III, p. 153, fig. 29.
Lent by the Hon. Andrew Vanneck.

ENGLISH SCHOOL

320 A Group of Englishmen in Rome

Canvas.   35 × 52 in.   Coll: Sir Charles Turner at Kirkleatham; Sotheby's, 23rd March 1949, Lot 42 as by Reynolds.   Lit: Denys Sutton "The Roman Caricatures of Reynolds", *Country Life Annual*, 1956, repr. Pl. 6.   This group of Englishmen against the background of the Colosseum and the Arch of Constantine has been attributed to Reynolds.   It has also been attributed to Nathaniel Dance to whose work, apart from a similarity of subject, it bears no resemblance (see No. 321).   Mr. Sutton has tentatively advanced the more probable name of James Russel but comparison with his only authenticated conversation piece of William Drake of Shardeloes is not conclusive.   This picture came from the collection of Sir Charles Turner of Kirkleatham who also owned a caricature group by Reynolds in which he figures.   His ownership of this painting suggests that he may also have been depicted in this group and Mr. Sutton has tentatively identified him together with Lord Charlemont and other of Reynolds's patrons.   If these identifications are correct then the painting must belong to the years 1749–52.
Lent by the Hon. Mrs. Ionides.

NEO-CLASSIC

NATHANIEL DANCE, R.A. (1735–1811)

321 Mr. Lippyat and the Duke of Northumberland in Rome

Canvas. 37¼ × 27½ in. Signed and dated: *N. Dance p. 1763.* Lit:
S. Sitwell, *Conversation Pieces*, London 1936, repr. p. 94. Hugh, 2nd
Duke of Northumberland (1742–1817) as Lord Percy, with his tutor,
Mr. Lippyat. Lord Percy served as a volunteer in the Seven Years'
War and afterwards commanded the 5th Regiment of Foot; served in
the American War of Independence and was promoted to Lieut.-
General. Succeeded to the dukedom in 1786. Mr. Lippyat is prob-
ably the Revd. Jonathan Lipyeatt who appears in Thomas Patch's
Punch Party, dated Florence 1760, and also in *Antiquaries at Pola*,
1760. In the latter picture he is seen with Jacob Houblon to
whom he was companion-tutor (see F. J. B. Watson, "Thomas
Patch", *Walpole Society*, Vol. 28, p. 32). Nathaniel Dance was in
Rome from 1754 to 1765. From 1760 onwards he painted a number
of groups of Englishmen, sometimes as in this picture against the
Colosseum, sometimes with St. Peter's in the background (see *Burling-
ton Magazine*, December 1955).
Lent by the Duke of Northumberland.

MICHAEL FOYE (Active 1765–1777)

322 Allan Ramsay

Marble bust. H. 24 in. Signed and indistinctly dated: *M. Foye
sculpt. Rome 177–* . Coll: Lockhart-Thomson. Lit: Alastair
Smart, *Allan Ramsay*, London 1952, p. 157. Allan Ramsay (1713–84),
who in 1761 was appointed principal painter to George III, paid four
visits to Italy. This bust was probably executed in Rome on his third
visit from 1775 to 1777. It is singularly appropriate that he should
have been portrayed in Roman dress for by this time, as Smart says,
"the scholar and writer in Ramsay had long since gained ascendancy
over the artist", and his time was largely devoted to research into the
problem of the site of Horace's Sabine villa, or as Fuseli puts it, tracing
"on dubious vestiges the haunts of ancient genius and learning".
Michael Foye, an Irish sculptor, came to Rome in 1773. He was still
there in 1777 when he sent from Rome to the Society of Artists "A
Busto of an Artist". This may be the bust of Allan Ramsay, but it
could also be that of James Durno, an Irish painter, whom Foye is
also known to have sculpted in Rome.
Lent by the Scottish National Portrait Gallery.

89

LECTURE ROOM

JAMES ("ATHENIAN") STUART (1713–1788)

323 A Set of Wall Decorations

Eight canvas panels, each 144 × 54 in., and fourteen canvas strips, each 144 × 18 in. Lit: Christopher Hussey, Article III on Ashburnham Place, Sussex, *Country Life*, 30th April 1953, repr. p. 1336. Christopher Hussey (*op. cit.*) says that these wall decorations, formerly in the drawing-room at Ashburnham Place, Sussex, resemble so closely in style "the painted room *c.* 1765, at Spencer House, London, that they must be ascribed to the same artist—James ('Athenian') Stuart. The pilaster strips of gilded scrolls are identical in both rooms, and the panels of arabesques containing basso relievos and medallions of mythology in full colour are unmistakably by the same hand". Hussey also points out that as there was said to be a flock wallpaper of *c.* 1800 behind these panels the implication is that they were superimposed later and may therefore have been executed for the London house and transferred to Ashburnham Place in the XIXth Century. Stuart's fame (which earned him the nickname "Athenian") was due to his publication with Nicholas Revett, and with the help of the Dilettanti Society, of the *Antiquities of Athens*, the first volume of which appeared in 1762. H. M. Colvin (*Dictionary of Architects*, 1954, p. 582) considers that the effect of this on contemporary English architecture has been much exaggerated. He points out that the first volume was devoted "to the different Greek modes of decorating buildings" and that the "Gusto Greco" of the 1760's was decorative rather than structural in character. Over 25 years were to elapse before the publication of the splendours of the Acropolis which, as the first accurate survey of the Athenian buildings, made its appearance a major event in the history of classical archaeology.
Lent by Messrs. Ayer and Co., Ltd., Bath.

324 Painted Boudoir Cabinet

48 × 26 × 12 in., *c.* 1790. Decorated with figure subjects and floral motifs on straw-coloured ground; doors enclose drawers. Lit: P. MacQuoid, *English Furniture . . . in the Lady Lever Art Gallery*, London 1928, No. 339, Pls. 83, 84. *D.E.F.*, I, p. 197, figs. 69, 70: pp. 192, 196.
Lent by the Lady Lever Art Gallery.

325 Wedgwood Pottery: Jasper Vase with Cover

H. 10½ in. From Wedgwood's Etruria factory, 1790. (Marked *Wedg-*

wood.) Decorated with "Sacrifice to Ceres", white on black; scroll handles, applied acanthus leaves.
Lent by Messrs. Josiah Wedgwood & Sons Ltd.

326 Pair of Carved and Gilt Candelabra Stands

H. 76 in. Designed by James ("Athenian") Stuart for the Painted Room at Spencer House; the ormolu candlesticks by Mathew Boulton, *c.* 1765. Triangular pedestals painted with winged figures of victory: above, three gilt gryphons support each candelabrum. Lit: *D.E.F.*, III, pp. 161–2, fig. 14.
Lent by the Earl Spencer.

327 Pair of Pedestals and Vases

H. 47½ in. Designed by James Wyatt for the Etruscan Room at Heveningham Hall, *c.* 1795. Painted by Biagio Rebecca in Etruscan taste; metal candle branches spring from rams' heads at corners of frieze. Lit: *D.E.F.*, III, pp. 161–2, fig. 19.
Lent by the Hon. Andrew Vanneck.

328 Pair of Painted Chairs

37 × 19 × 16 in. Probably designed by James Wyatt for the Etruscan Room at Heveningham and painted by Biagio Rebecca, *c.* 1795. From a set of six; neo-classic detail in Etruscan taste; oval backs, caned seats.
Lent by the Hon. Andrew Vanneck.

329 Painted Commode

36 × 50 × 23 in., *c.* 1795. Serpentine front; ivory-coloured ground with green diaper pattern; gilt colonettes and bandings; ovals with figure subjects after Angelica Kauffmann and Adam Buck. Lit: *D.E.F.*, II, p. 122, Pl. IV: p. 125.
Lent by the Duke of Norfolk.

330 Wedgwood Pottery: Black Basalt Vase

H. 10 in. From Wedgwood's Etruria factory, 1775. Marked *Wedgwood and Bentley.* Applied husk festoons, scale horn handles, mask terminals.
Lent by Messrs. Josiah Wedgwood & Sons Ltd.

331 Wedgwood Pottery: Black Basalt Vase

H. 14 in. From Wedgwood's Etruria factory, 1774. Marked *Wedgwood and Bentley.* Scroll handles, applied masks and festoons.
Lent by Messrs. Josiah Wedgwood & Sons Ltd.

332 Wedgwood Pottery: Black Basalt Vase

H. 12 in. From Wedgwood's Etruria factory, 1775. Marked *Wedgwood and Bentley*. Mask terminals, scale horn handles.
Lent by Messrs. Josiah Wedgwood & Sons Ltd.

333 Hall Chair

41 × 23 × 18 in. Probably made by Thomas Chippendale from a design by Robert Adam for Nostell Priory, *c.* 1766. From a set. Painted beechwood: oval back, coat of arms in centre of radiating pattern, wheat-ear decoration; shaped seat and curved arms; fluted legs with paterae at corners of seat rail. Lit: Oliver Brackett, *Thomas Chippendale*, London 1924, p. 264, Pl. LV. *D.E.F.* I, pp. 316–17, fig. 3.
Lent by the Hon. Rowland Winn.

334 Satinwood Upright Secretaire

54 × 35 × 16 in. Probably designed by Robert Adam. Attributed to Thomas Chippendale, *c.* 1770–75. Inlaid with various woods on satinwood ground; oval panel of reclining nymph in ivory on ebony ground; frieze drawer, fall-front, lower portion enclosed by doors; canted angles with pendant husks. Lit: *D.E.F.*, I, p. 153, fig. 64: p. 147.
Lent by the Earl of Harewood.

335 Wedgwood Pottery: Vase and Cover with Surface Marbling

H. 13 in. From Wedgwood's Etruria factory, 1772. Marked *Wedgwood and Bentley*. Marbling in form of agate; snake handles and applied satyr terminals; white Jasper plinth.
Lent by Messrs. Josiah Wedgwood & Sons Ltd.

336 Pair of Gilt Mahogany Tripods with Ormolu Vases

H. 67 in. Style of Robert Adam; the mounts by Mathew Boulton, *c.* 1765–70. Rams-heads decoration; branches for two lights.
Lent by the Hon. Mrs. Ionides.

337 Overmantel Mirror in Painted Frame

88 × 59½ in., *c.* 1790. Wood frame painted cream colour; carved gilt ornament, ovals in grisaille on black ground. Lit: *D.E.F.*, II, p. 354, fig. 112.
Lent by Lt.-Col. A. Heywood-Lonsdale.

338   Carved and Gilt Console Table

33 × 62 × 28 in.   Probably designed by Robert Adam.   Attributed to Thomas Chippendale, c. 1770.   Semi-circular satinwood top inlaid with various woods; four scroll ram-headed supports suspending husk festoons and ending in hoof feet.   Lit: *D.E.F.*, III, p. 296, fig. 64.
Lent by the Earl of Harewood.

339   Blue-John and Ormolu Perfume Burner

H. 22½ in.   The mounts by Mathew Boulton, c. 1770.   Vase, with pineapple knop and rim banded with ormolu, supported by three winged gryphons on base with festoon of bay leaves.   Coll: Lowther Castle.
Lent by Ralph Dutton, Esq.

340   Upright Secretaire

52½ × 34 × 16½ in., c. 1777.   In French taste; inlaid with various woods on satinwood, with urns, festoons, rosettes, vases of flowers and a trophy in oval panels; frieze drawers; fall front, lower portion enclosed by doors; canted angles with floral sprays.
Lent by the Trustees of the Earl of Chichester.

341   Wedgwood Pottery: Vase with Surface Marbling

H. 16 in.   From Wedgwood's Etruria factory, 1783.   Marked *Wedgwood*.   Reversible cover, applied arabesque border, white Jasper plinth.
Lent by Messrs. Josiah Wedgwood & Sons Ltd.

342   Rosewood Pole-screen

H. 59½ in.   Probably designed by Henry Holland, c. 1800.   Carved and gilt enrichments, panel painted with arabesques in water-colours, by Louis André Delabrière.   Lit: *D.E.F.*, III, p. 66, fig. 34: p. 68.
Lent by Major Simon Whitbread.

343   Painted Commode

42½ × 44 × 19½ in., c. 1790.   Semi-circular; painted top; ground of panels pea-green; ovals with figure subjects after Angelica Kauffmann.   Lit: P. MacQuoid, *English Furniture . . . in the Lady Lever Art Gallery*, London 1928, No. 347, Pl. 86.   *D.E.F.*, II, p. 124, fig. 37: p. 125.
Lent by the Lady Lever Art Gallery.

344 Wedgwood Pottery: Black Basalt Wine Vase

H. 16 in. From Wedgwood's Etruria factory, 1778. Marked *Wedgwood and Bentley*. Figure of Bacchus holding spout; applied goat head and vine wreath ("Sacred to Bacchus").
Lent by Messrs. Josiah Wedgwood & Sons Ltd.

345 Wedgwood Pottery: Black Basalt Lamp

H. 14 in. From Wedgwood's Etruria factory, 1783. Marked *Wedgwood*. With three burners and applied arabesque decoration. Known as the "Michael Angelo Vase".
Lent by Messrs. Josiah Wedgwood & Sons Ltd.

346 Wedgwood Pottery: Black Basalt Water Vase

H. 16 in. From Wedgwood's Etruria factory, 1778. Marked *Wedgwood and Bentley*. Figure of Neptune holding spout; applied dolphin head and seaweed wreath ("Sacred to Neptune").
Lent by Messrs. Josiah Wedgwood & Sons Ltd.

347 Drawing-room Chair

33 × 18 × 18 in., *c.* 1795. In gilt wood with circular seat; the back with fluted columns supporting panel painted by Louis André Delabrière. Lit: *D.E.F.*, II, fig. 259, p. 306.
Lent by Major Simon Whitbread.

348 Inlaid Commode

34 × 50 × 24 in. Probably by Thomas Chippendale, *c.* 1770. Veneered with mahogany; inlaid with coloured garlands, baskets of flowers and trophies in tulipwood and stained harewood; ormolu mounts (the mounts from the same casts as a commode at Nostell Priory, supplied by Thomas Chippendale, 1770). Lit: MacQuoid, *Age of Satinwood*, pp. 34–5, fig. 28.
Lent by the Marquess of Salisbury.

349 Wedgwood Pottery: Pair of Vases with Surface Marbling

H. 14½ in. From Wedgwood's Etruria factory, 1772. Marked *Wedgwood and Bentley*. Snake handles, applied acanthus leaves, white Jasper plinths.
Lent by Messrs. Josiah Wedgwood & Sons Ltd.

350 Wedgwood Pottery: The Portland Vase (Jasper Ware)

H. 11 in., *c.* 1790. The Portland vase was lent by the Duke of Portland to Wedgwood in 1786 for the purpose of making the copy.
Lent by Messrs. Josiah Wedgwood & Sons Ltd.

351 Pair of Carved and Gilt Pedestals

H. 48 in. Designed by Henry Holland for the Throne Room at Carlton House, *c.* 1795. From a set of eight; round-fronted, fluted, with classical decoration; terminal figures at sides; originally supporting large ormolu candelabra. Lit: H. Clifford Smith, *Buckingham Palace*, London 1931, p. 141, Pls. 142–3, 155–6.
Lent by Her Majesty The Queen (Buckingham Palace).

JOSEPH NOLLEKENS, R.A. (1737–1823)
352 William Weddell

Marble bust. H. 34 in. Signed: *Nollekens F^t.*. Lit: H. Honour, "Newby Hall, Yorkshire," *The Connoisseur*, CXXXIV, 1954, p. 251, No. 10. William Weddell (d. 1792) acquired Newby Hall soon after 1750 and it is to him that is owed much of its present character. The work was begun when, shortly after his return from Italy in 1766, he commissioned Robert Adam to design a gallery for the sculpture he had acquired abroad. A similar bust by Nollekens, done in 1789, is placed on the monument to Weddell in Ripon Minster.
Lent by Major Edward Compton.

353 Pair of Silver Candelabra

H. 18½ in. By John Parsons, 1791. Fluted baluster stems and two branches.
Lent by the Worshipful Company of Mercers.

354 Pair of Lustres

25½ × 16 in., *c.* 1785. Porcelain bases with inset ormolu decoration; two candle branches; festoons of drops.
Lent by Mrs. Lindsay-Fynn.

JAMES BARRY, R.A. (1741–1806)
355 Self-portrait

Canvas. 30 × 25 in. Lit: R. R. Wark, "Iconography and Date of James Barry's Self-portrait", *Burlington Magazine*, XCVI, 1954, pp. 153–4, fig. 27; E. K. Waterhouse, *Painting in Britain*, 1953, p. 199. Barry is described on his tomb-slab in St. Paul's Cathedral as "The Great Historical Painter". His series of large canvases in the Great

Room of the Royal Society of Arts must still, as Professor Waterhouse writes (*op. cit.*), "be accounted the most considerable achievement in the true 'grand style' by any British painter of the century". The series was painted between 1777 and 1783. The years 1766 to 1771 Barry spent in Italy "saturating himself only too faithfully", as Waterhouse says, "in the ancients and in Michelangelo". Wark (*op. cit.*) shows that this self-portrait is connected with the self-portrait in the *Visitors at Olympia* at the Royal Society of Arts which was painted about 1780. But he shows that whereas No. 355 was probably begun at that date it was not completed until 1803. The iconography of this picture is complicated but, as Wark shows, Barry has presented himself as the Greek artist Timanthes holding a conjectural reconstruction of a picture of a sleeping cyclops for which that artist was famous. The portion of the statue in the top left-hand corner is probably the foot of Hercules crushing the Snake of Envy, perhaps an allusion to the fact that in his devotion to "history painting" he had cause to envy the wealth of the portraitists of his day.
Lent by the National Gallery of Ireland.

NATHANIEL DANCE, R.A. (1734–1816)
356 Timon of Athens
Canvas. $48\frac{1}{2} \times 54$ in. Coll: in a Windsor inventory of 1776 as by Dance. Exh: Society of Artists, 1767, No. 43. R.A., Winter, 1951, No. 3. Engraved by Hall, published Boydell, 1771 (as in the Royal Collection). From Shakespeare, Act IV, Scene IV. Nathaniel Dance was in Rome from about 1754 to 1765, where he painted a number of groups of Englishmen on the Grand Tour (see No. 321). In Rome he would certainly have been aware of the neo-classical paintings of Gavin Hamilton. He knew Mengs, against whom he is said to have conceived some prejudice, and through Angelica Kauffmann, with whom he was madly in love at the time, he may have met Winckelmann, whose portrait she painted. This picture, exhibited two years after his return from Rome and possibly painted earlier, clearly shows Dance working in the neo-classical style.
Lent by Her Majesty The Queen (Hampton Court).

357 Inlaid Writing-table
$41 \times 34 \times 17\frac{1}{2}$ in., *c.* 1775. Veneered with rosewood, banded with mahogany; cupboard doors of superstructure inlaid with classical figures; honeysuckle ornament on frieze, tripods at sides; top and shelf with brass galleries.
Lent by the National Trust (Stourhead).

358 Pair of Blue-John and Ormolu Candlesticks

H. 9 in., c. 1765–70. In form of urns on plinths.
Lent by Mrs. David Gubbay.

359 Wedgwood Pottery: Jasper Vase

H. 14 in. From Wedgwood's Etruria factory, 1782. Marked *Wedgwood*. Decorated with "Chariot of Venus", white on blue; applied acanthus leaves, white Jasper plinth.
Lent by Messrs. Josiah Wedgwood & Sons Ltd.

360 Pair of Satinwood Pedestals and Marble Vases

H. 52 in. Pedestals made by John Cobb for Mr. Paul Methuen, 1772. Baluster shape, inlaid decoration of various woods. Designed to accompany Serpentine Commode, No. 361. The vases of white marble with ormolu mounts were supplied by Harrache, London. Lit: *D.E.F.*, III, p. 160, fig. 8.
Lent by Lord Methuen.

361 Inlaid Satinwood Commode

36 × 54 × 27½ in. Made by John Cobb for Mr. Paul Methuen in 1772. Serpentine front, veneered with satinwood and inlaid with various woods; top painted in imitation marble; ormolu mounts. (See No. 360.) Exh: *B.F.A.C.*, Winter 1938, No. 4. Lit: R. Edwards and M. Jourdain, *Georgian Cabinet-Makers*, 3rd Edition, 1955, p. 156, fig. 71.
Lent by Lord Methuen.

362 Silver-gilt Cup

H. 16¼ in. By James Young and Orlando Jackson, 1774–75. In form of classic urn; lid with acanthus chasing and pine cone knop; body in relief with swags, masks and rings; vine stalk and leaf handles; with arms of George Templer and his wife, Jane Paul.
Lent by C. D. Rotch, Esq.

363 The Richmond Cup (Silver-gilt)

H. 19 in. Designed by Robert Adam; made by David Smith and Robert Sharp, 1770. Urn-shaped, with winged caryatid handles; frieze representing a race and medallions showing jockeys saddling up and racing. The original design is in the Soane Museum. The Richmond Gold Cup was first run for, over a distance of four miles, in 1759. The present cup, of 1770, was won by Mr. Bell's horse, "Denmark".
Lent by the Marquess of Zetland.

364 Silver-gilt Cup

H. 13 in. By Thomas Heming, 1771. Oval; lower part of body plated, with medallion depicting figures in early XVIIIth Century costume drinking round a table; handles draped with serpents; infant Bacchus on cover.

Lent by C. D. Rotch, Esq.

GAVIN HAMILTON (1723–1798)

365 Dr. John Moore, Douglas, 8th Duke of Hamilton, and Ensign John Moore in Rome

Canvas. 83 × 60 in. Lit: Carola Oman, *Sir John Moore*, repr. facing p. 34; *Burlington Magazine*, December 1955, repr. In 1772 Douglas, 8th Duke of Hamilton (1756–1799) set out on the Grand Tour accompanied by Dr. John Moore (1730–1802) as his medical attendant, tutor and travelling companion, and by the latter's son John Moore (1761–1809), the future hero of Corunna. They remained abroad four years, returning to England in 1776. They were in Rome from about November 1775 until May 1776, and it was during these months that this portrait group was begun. It was not finished until August 1777. (Letter from Tom Pelham to his father, British Museum A.D.MS. 33127). They are depicted on an eminence overlooking the Forum, the Campo Vaccino as it was then called. On their right is the Temple of Concord, on the entablature of which can be read part of the inscription:

SENATVS. POPVL (*vsqve. Romanvs*)
INCENDIO. CONS (*vmptvm. Restitvit*)

At the far end of the Campo Vaccino can be seen, from left to right, the Colosseum, the Church of S. Maria Nuova, and the Arch of Titus; in the distance the Alban Hills. Gavin Hamilton is best known as an excavator and dealer in antiquities, and as one of the earliest exponents of the neo-classical school. Unfortunately the size and position of his classical paintings in the Palace of Holyroodhouse and at Althorp presented too many difficulties for it to be possible to include them in this exhibition.

Lent by the Duke of Hamilton.

JOHN HAMILTON MORTIMER, A.R.A. (1741(?)–1779)

366 The Hero Decides to Seek his Fortune

Canvas. 30 × 25 in. Coll: purchased 1948. Exh: Society of Artists, 1775, No. 178. Lit: E. K. Waterhouse, *Painting in Britain*, London 1953, p. 210, Pl. 177. No. 1 from a set of four; a moral tale, entitled

"The Progress of Virtue". Mortimer's own "Progress of Virtue" seems to have started in the same year in which this set was exhibited at the Society of Artists for, according to Redgrave, he married in 1775 and abandoned those vicious habits which had shattered by their excesses a strong frame and handsome person. Mortimer is the only artist in the Neo-Classic Room who did not visit Italy but in this picture, at any rate, he appears to have succumbed to the prevailing taste by presenting his hero in Roman attire.

Lent by the Tate Gallery.

ANGELICA KAUFFMANN, R.A. (1741–1807)

367 Rinaldo and Armida

Canvas. Oval, 50 × 40 in. Coll: bequeathed by Ernest Cook to the N.A.C.F. in 1955 and presented to Kenwood. Engr. T. Burke. Angelica Kauffmann painted two pictures of *Rinaldo and Armida* from Tasso's *Gerusalemme Liberata*. The first from Canto XVII was painted in 1772, the second from Canto XX in 1775.

Lent by the London County Council (Iveagh Bequest, Kenwood).

368 Mahogany Library Table

36½ × 33 × 18½ in., *c.* 1770. Carved in neo-classic taste; superstructure of drawers flanking central compartment with circles sunk in top for bases of two candlesticks. Lit: *D.E.F.*, III, p. 256, fig. 35: p. 261.

Lent by Lord Fairhaven.

369 Vase-shaped Mantel Clock

H. 29 in. By Vulliamy, *c.* 1795. Case veneered with satinwood, inlaid with rosewood; painted in grisaille; ormolu mounts. Exh: Ormeley Lodge, Ham Common, *Masterpieces of British Art and Craftsmanship*, 1954, No. 148. Lit: *D.E.F.*, II, pp. 102–3, fig. 68.

Lent by the Governor and Company of the Bank of England.

JOSEPH NOLLEKENS, R.A. (1737–1823)

370 George III

Marble bust. H. 24 in. Signed *NOLLEKENS Ft. A. MDCCLXXIII.* Inscribed: *GEORGIUS III PATRONUS MUNIFICUS.* Coll: commissioned by the Royal Society in 1773. Exh: R.A. 1774, No. 190; R.A., Winter 1951, No. 372.

Lent by the Royal Society.

ANGELICA KAUFFMANN, R.A. (1741–1807)

371 Philip Tisdall and Family

Canvas. 61 × 74 in. Philip Tisdall (1703–77), Irish politician, became successively Solicitor-General, Attorney-General, principal Secretary of State and Keeper of the Seal. He is seen with, from left to right, his eldest daughter Elizabeth (d. 1823) who married in 1760 Hugh Morgan of Cottles Town and Cork Abbey, Colonel of 98th Regiment; his daughter Mary who died unmarried; Catherine, only child and heiress of Colonel Hugh Morgan, who married in 1785 Robert Stearne Tighe; and his wife, Mary Singleton, co-heiress of the Rt. Hon. Henry Singleton, P.C., of Aclare, whom he married in 1736. The Tisdalls were amongst Angelica Kauffmann's patrons when she visited Ireland in 1771. According to Manners and Williamson (*Kauffmann*, 1924, pp. 38, 39) she painted portraits of Tisdall and his wife, and of his two daughters, and later on replicas of Tisdall himself for other members of his family. This group is not specifically mentioned but the approximate ages of the sitters would agree with this date. The inscription *Et in Arcadia Ego* on the urn to right occurs in XVIIth-Century pictorial art in the paintings of Guercino and Nicholas Poussin and deals with the transience of human existence (see E. Panofsky's essay on the subject published in *Philosophy and History*, edited by R. Klibansky and H. J. Paton, 1936). In the XVIIIth Century the theme was taken up by both Wilson and Reynolds. The latter's painting of *Mrs. Bouverie and Mrs. Crewe* was exhibited at the R.A. in 1769 (91) and Angelica could have taken the idea of the inscription from this picture. After the inscription appears a date, not easily decipherable, but which could be read as *36*. If this reading is correct then the inscription refers to the date of their marriage but it may also imply a honeymoon visit to Italy. The elaborate chair recalls Robert Manwaring's designs for garden seats published in *The Cabinet and Chair Maker's Real Friend and Companion*, 1765.

Lent by the Hon. Mrs. Ionides.

372 Pianoforte in Mahogany Case

32½ × 62 × 24 in. By William Southwell, *c*. 1785. Veneered with satinwood, yew and other woods in case of elliptical form. Lit: Philip James, *Early Key-board Instruments*, 1930, Pl. 59.

Lent by the Hon. Mrs. Ionides.

373 Pair of Pedestals and Marble Urns

H. 68 in., *c.* 1775. Pinewood, painted blue and white, with carved ornament in neo-classic taste. Surmounted by white marble urns decorated with masks and medallions with figures.
Lent by the Hon. Mrs. Ionides.

374 Inlaid Satinwood Commode

35½ × 58 × 24¾ in. Attributed to Thomas Chippendale, *c.* 1770. Classical design ; doors veneered with satinwood banded with mahogany and tulipwood, ovals inlaid with flowers in vases ; pilasters mounted in ormolu with ram-headed capitals. Lit: P. MacQuoid, *English Furniture . . . in the Lady Lever Art Gallery*, London 1924, No. 327, Pl. 78. *D.E.F.*, II, p. 119, fig. 22 : pp. 110, 116.
Lent by the Lady Lever Art Gallery.

375 Silver-gilt Cup and Cover

H. 18½ in. Maker's mark: *R.M./B.S.*, *c.* 1773. Oval with floral swags ; beaded loop handles, fluted cover. Presented by Sir Frank Newson-Smith, Bt.
Lent by the Corporation of London.

376 Silver-gilt Cup

H. 15¾ in. By J. Wakelin and W. Taylor, 1778. Oval, with festoons of vines ; loop handles, cover surmounted by artichoke.
Lent by C. D. Rotch, Esq.

377 Doncaster Race Cup (Silver-gilt)

H. 19 in. By J. Wakelin and W. Taylor, 1786. Oval ; sides set with medallions representing jockeys saddling up and racing ; loop handles, cover surmounted by artichoke. Presented to Birmingham Art Gallery by Miss Margaret Pugh, 1942. Exh: Goldsmiths' Hall, *Corporation Plate of England and Wales*, 1952, No. 153.
Lent by the Corporation of Birmingham.

GEORGE ROMNEY (1734–1802)

378 Viscountess Bulkeley as Hebe

Canvas. 94 × 58 in. Lit.: F. Saxl and R. Wittkower, *British Art and the Mediterranean*, 1948, repr. 63 (4). Elizabeth Harriet (1759–1826), daughter and heiress of Sir George Warren of Poynton, married Thomas James, 7th Viscount Bulkeley, in 1777. The date of the

painting is given as 1776, the year before her marriage. Romney painted the portrait of her husband in Rome in 1773. As Professor Wittkower points out (*op. cit.*), the classical allusion is no more than a flattering reference to the young beauty, a mere convention which does not interfere with the strict rules of the age of taste. Hebe is the goddess of youth, who fills the cups of the gods with nectar. She is shown here pointing to a vessel while the eagle of Zeus appears from above. The fashion of representing a beautiful woman as Hebe was introduced by Sir Joshua Reynolds, and was followed many times by contemporary artists.
Lent by Sir Richard Williams-Bulkeley, Bt.

379 Mahogany Chair

38 × 25½ × 21 in. Made by Thomas Chippendale for Nostell Priory, *c.* 1768. From a set of six. Square back with lyre-shaped splat; the "carving exceeding rich in the antique taste". Lit: Oliver Brackett, *Thomas Chippendale*, London 1924, p. 176. Pl. XIX.
Lent by the Hon. Rowland Winn.

380 Pair of Mahogany Armchairs

37 × 23 × 21 in., *c.* 1780. From a set. Decorated with paterae and foliage in holly wood; top rail centring in Wedgwood plaque. Lit: *D.E.F.*, I, p. 296, fig. 223: p. 293.
Lent by the Earl of Yarborough.

381 Mahogany Writing-table

37½ × 32½ × 25 in., *c.* 1785. Veneered and decorated with marquetry of various woods; desk enclosed by cylindrical sliding top. Lit: *D.E.F.*, III, p. 258, fig. 42: p. 263.
Lent by the Duke of Northumberland.

ANGELICA KAUFFMANN, R.A. (1741–1807)

382 The Disarming of Cupid

Canvas. Diam. 25 in. Coll: bequeathed by Ernest Cook to the N.A.C.F. in 1955 and presented to Kenwood. Two other versions of this subject which has also been entitled *Three Nymphs Distressing Cupid*, have been in American sales in recent years. A painting of the subject was engraved in 1777 by William Wynne Ryland as *Etiam Amor Criminibus Plectitur*. It was probably from this that the design was taken from which S. S. Spengler modelled a porcelain

group (Derby biscuit porcelain: Victoria and Albert Museum, No.
C.59—1924). Miss Anne Crookshank has kindly supplied this
information.
Lent by the London County Council (Iveagh Bequest, Kenwood).

BENJAMIN WEST, P.R.A. (1738–1820)
383   Cyrus Liberating the Family of Astyages
Canvas. 41 × 54 in. Signed and dated: *B. West 1770.* Coll:
Buckingham House (undated inventory of George III: "Relates
to the History of Cyrus"). Lit: J. Galt, *Benjamin West,* London
1820, Vol. II, pp. 50–1. Pair to No. 395. Part of the series of
classical subjects commissioned by George III, formerly in the Warm
Room at Buckingham House. See No 385.
Lent by Her Majesty The Queen (Kensington Palace).

384   Pair of Painted Sideboard Pedestals and Urns
H. 58 in., *c.* 1775. Designed by Robert Adam for Sir Watkins
Williams-Wynn, 20 St. James's Square, built 1771–74. Painted
mahogany; the pedestals, supporting classical urns, decorated with
medallions; rams' heads at frieze corners. En suite with No. 386.
Lent by the National Museum of Wales.

BENJAMIN WEST, P.R.A. (1738–1820)
385   Hannibal Swearing Never to Make Peace with Rome
Canvas. 59 × 121 in. Signed and dated: *B. West Pinxit 1770.*
Coll: Buckingham House (undated inventory of George III). Lit:
J. Galt, *Benjamin West,* London 1820, Vol. II, p. 45. Benjamin West
was born in Pennsylvania and went to Italy to study art where he
spent the years 1760–63. He was the first American painter to come to
Rome where his arrival caused inordinate curiosity. When he went to
the Vatican he was accompanied by thirty carriages and his pro-
nouncement that the Apollo Belvedere resembled a young Mohawk
must have caused some astonishment. West, too, might have been
astonished had he known that Cardinal Albani, who was blind, had
enquired whether he was white or black and clearly expected a Red
Indian. In Rome he worked diligently and came into contact with
the circle of Mengs and Gavin Hamilton and was no doubt influenced
by the precepts on history painting of Winckelmann. On leaving
Italy he set up in London as a portrait painter. He achieved considerable success with his neo-classical canvases, and George III so

admired his *Departure of Regulus* (Exhibited R.A., 1769, No. 120) that he commissioned this work as a pendant. These two works, together with Nos. 383 and 395, formed part of the decoration of classical scenes in the Warm Room of Buckingham House. Three other historical pictures, *The Death of Bayard*, *The Death of Epaminondas*, and *The Death of Wolfe* completed the series. When West abandoned classical subjects for contemporary history and painted *The Death of Wolfe*, 1771, in contemporary costume, even Reynolds was forced to admit that a revolution in art had taken place.
Lent by Her Majesty The Queen (Kensington Palace).

386   Mahogany Sideboard

36 × 96 × 42 in., *c.* 1775. Designed by Robert Adam for Sir Watkin Williams-Wynn, 20 St. James's Square, built 1771–74. Legs and frieze painted and fluted. En suite with No. 384. Lit: A. T. Bolton, *The Architecture of Robert and James Adam*, London 1922, Vol. II, p. 60 (Repr.).
Lent by the National Museum of Wales.

387   Pair of Blue-John and Ormolu Ewers

H. 19 in. The mounts by Mathew Boulton, *c.* 1765–70. With masks of Pan.
Lent by the City Museum and Art Gallery, Birmingham.

388   Pair of Blue-John and Ormolu Candelabra

H. 15½ in. The mounts by Mathew Boulton, *c.* 1765–70. Two looped branches; reversible covers.
Lent by the City Museum and Art Gallery, Birmingham.

389   Blue-John and Ormolu Candelabrum

H. 18 in. The mounts by Mathew Boulton, *c.* 1765–70. Ormolu male terminal figures supporting six candle branches.
Lent Anonymously.

390   Rosewood Winecooler

27 × 30 × 22 in. Probably designed by Robert Adam; made by Thomas Chippendale, *c.* 1770. Oval, with lifting top, on tapering legs; mounted with ormolu. En suite with sideboard and pedestals at Harewood. Lit: *D.E.F.*, III, p. 129, fig. 15.
Lent by the Earl of Harewood.

391 **Inlaid Satinwood Commode**

36 × 45 × 21 in. By William Gates for the Prince of Wales's apartments at Buckingham Palace, 1781. One of a pair. Semi-circular, inlaid with various coloured woods; ovals and top decorated with fluted vases. Lit: H. Clifford Smith, *Buckingham Palace*, London 1931, p. 225, Pl. 86. *D.E.F.*, II, p. 122, fig. 31.
Lent by Her Majesty The Queen (Buckingham Palace).

392 **Pair of Pastille Burners**

H. 13½ in. Probably designed by Robert Adam, *c.* 1770. Ormolu mounts; winged griffin supports with festoons of foliage on rectangular bases.
Lent by the Earl of Harewood.

393 **Silver-gilt Tea-kettle and Stand**

H. 5¾ in. By Andrew Fogelberg and Stephen Gilbert, 1784. Oval with rounded body resting in detachable stand; wave ornament on lid and upper part of body; bone handle, conical spout.
Lent by C. D. Rotch, Esq.

ANGELICA KAUFFMANN, R.A. (1741–1807)

394 **The Artist in the Character of Design Listening to the Inspiration of Poetry**

Canvas. Diam. 24 in. Inscribed: *For George Bowles, Esq.* in top left-hand corner. Coll: bequeathed by Ernest Cook to the N.A.C.F. in 1955 and presented to Kenwood. Engr: T. Burke, 1787. Angelica Kauffman was in Italy from 1763 to 1766 where she certainly came into contact with the neo-classic movement since in 1764 she painted the portrait of Winckelmann. She returned to Italy in 1781 and spent most of the rest of her life at Rome. There are many painted ceilings and decorative works attributed to Angelica throughout England but there are only two cases in which decorative paintings can be assigned to her with certainty; two overdoors at Knowsley, previously at Grosvenor Square, and the roundels in the entrance hall of Burlington House, which were painted for Somerset House, and for which accounts are in the possession of the Royal Academy (see Miss Anne Crookshank's *Catalogue of the Exhibition of Paintings by Angelica Kauffmann*, Kenwood, 1955). Angelica lists this picture as having been painted in Rome in 1782 for Mr. Bowles.
Lent by the London County Council (Iveagh Bequest, Kenwood).

LECTURE ROOM

BENJAMIN WEST, P.R.A. (1738–1820)

395 The Wife of Arminius brought Captive to Germanicus

Canvas. 41 × 54 in. Signed and dated: *B. West 1770.* Coll: Buckingham House (undated inventory of George III). Lit: J. Galt, *Benjamin West*, London 1820, Vol. II, pp. 50–1. Pair to No. 383. Part of the series of classical subjects, commissioned by George III, formerly in the Warm Room at Buckingham House. See No. 385.
Lent by Her Majesty The Queen (Kensington Palace).

SIR JOSHUA REYNOLDS, P.R.A. (1723–1792)

396 Mrs. Peter Beckford: A Sacrifice to Hygeia

Canvas. 94 × 58 in. Coll: William Beckford of Fonthill; Duke of Hamilton; Hamilton Palace Sale, Christie's, 6th November 1919, Lot 50; Viscount Leverhulme. Exh: possibly R.A., 1782 (116). Lit: J. W. Oliver, *William Beckford*, 1932, pp. 74–5, 159; E. K. Waterhouse, *Reynolds*, London, 1941, p. 73, Pl. 235. Louisa, daughter of Lord Rivers, married Peter Beckford, the author of *Thoughts on Hunting*. She had little sympathy with his tastes and formed a passionate friendship with his cousin, William Beckford, the author of *Vathek*. As the sitter was in ill-health at the time when her portrait was painted Reynolds represented her as paying a libation to Hygeia, the goddess of health. Two years later, in 1784, she wrote to William Beckford that Mesmer had cured her "but unluckily for me the waters of oblivion are not part of his remedy". She died in 1791. For Reynolds's attitude towards the antique and the use of classical draperies and symbols, see the Introduction.
Lent by the Lady Lever Art Gallery.

397 Inlaid Chest of Drawers on Stand

33¾ × 48 × 23 in., *c.* 1775. Veneered with harewood and satinwood; inlaid in various woods with motifs in neo-classic taste; gilt mouldings, taper legs. Lit: *D.E.F.*, II, p. 52, Pl. 1.
Lent by the Duke of Northumberland.

398 Pair of Cut-glass Vases

H. 14½ in., *c.* 1795. Ovoid shape on square bases; ormolu mounts.
Lent by the Lady Elizabeth Byng.

399 Pair of Blue-John and Ormolu Urns

H. 11 in. The mounts by Mathew Boulton, *c.* 1765–70. Pine-cone knop, swags of flowers and masks in ormolu; green marble bases.
Lent by C. D. Rotch, Esq.

106

400 Two-handled Cup and Cover

H. 18½ in., By (?) Samuel Wheat, 1761. Decorated with acanthus, swags and frieze of vines. Presented by Professor Sir Albert E. Richardson, P.R.A., in 1950.
Lent by the Royal Academy of Arts.

401 Commode in French Taste

33 × 56 × 24½ in., *c.* 1770. Serpentine form, veneered with satinwood; front inlaid with bull on ebony oval, sides with classical amphorae; metal gadrooning at top, pendants, base and feet. Lit: P. MacQuoid, *English Furniture . . . in the Lady Lever Art Gallery*, London 1928, No. 329, Pl. 79. *D.E.F.*, II, p. 119, fig. 23: p. 116.
Lent by the Lady Lever Art Gallery.

402 Silver-gilt Epergne

H. 17 in. By Thomas Powell, 1777. Oval frame with eight branches supporting dishes and surmounted by large oval dish.
Lent by C. D. Rotch, Esq.

SIR JOSHUA REYNOLDS, P.R.A. (1723–1792)

403 Sir William Hamilton

Canvas. 100½ × 69 in. Coll: presented by the sitter to the British Museum, 1782. Exh: British Institution, 1831, No. 114. Lit: *National Gallery Catalogues, British School*, by Martin Davies, 1946, p. 116. Engr: H. Hudson, 1782. Sir William Hamilton, K.B. (1730–1803), was British envoy at Naples from 1764 to 1800. He is now chiefly remembered as the husband of Nelson's Emma Hart about whose arrival in Naples in 1786 James Byres wrote that Sir William "has lately got a piece of modernity which will fatigue and exhaust him more than all the volcanoes and antiquities in the Kingdom of Naples". But it is as a volcanist and antiquary that he deserves to be remembered. The British Museum acquired many of his antiquities: terracottas, bronzes, gold ornaments and ancient vases, and amongst the latter the large vase signed by Meidias which is shown in the picture. He also formed a collection of pictures (see *Burlington Magazine* Vol. LXXXII February 1943, where this picture is reproduced). His interest in the latest excavations at Herculaneum and Pompeii, which he supported "both by his enthusiasm and his purse", contributed greatly to the growing interest amongst Englishmen in classical antiquities. He also befriended many of the English artists who went to

Naples. This, and a very similar head-and-shoulders portrait belonging to the Dilettanti Society, presumably derive from sittings in June 1777 when Hamilton was in England, but the earliest firm date for the picture is 23rd February 1782 when it was received by the British Museum.

Lent by the National Portrait Gallery.

CHRISTOPHER HEWETSON (b. c. 1739)

404   The Duke of Gloucester

Marble bust. H. 23 in. Inscribed: *Chr. Hewetson fect. Romæ 1772.* William Henry, Duke of Gloucester (1743–1805), brother of George III, visited Rome in 1772. A letter in the *London Chronicle* for May 2, 1772, mentions that he was sitting to several artists. Amongst them "Pompeo Battoni (sic) paints him. Mr. Hewetson has modelled him in clay." Presumably this was a study for the marble bust at Windsor Castle which, as Mr. Francis Watson has pointed out (verbally), is the counterpart in marble to the portraits of Batoni. Hewetson came to Rome in 1765 and remained there until his death in 1798. His most important work was the monument in marble of Dr. Baldwin, Provost of Trinity College, Dublin. He is known to have sculpted a number of busts. That of Clement XIV (1773) is in the Victoria and Albert Museum, that of the Earl Bishop of Bristol is in the National Portrait Gallery. He is also known to have executed a bust of Gavin Hamilton. An account of Hewetson by Mr. Terence Hodgkinson will be published in the next volume of the *Walpole Society.*

Lent by Her Majesty The Queen (Windsor Castle).

ENGLISH SCHOOL (c. 1770)

405   Sir Rowland and Lady Winn in their Library

Canvas. 40 × 50 in. Lit: M. W. Brockwell, *The Nostell Collection,* London, 1915, No. 45. Sir Rowland Winn, 5th Bt. (1739–85) married Sabine, daughter of Baron d'Hervert in 1765. The attribution of the picture to Mercier (Brockwell, *op. cit.*), who died in 1760, is untenable. Furthermore the Library at Nostell, in which they are shown, was designed by Adam in 1766. The large library table in the picture was bought from Chippendale in 1767 and still shows the influence of Kent.

Lent by the Hon. Rowland Winn.

JOHN ZOFFANY, R.A. (1735–1810)

406 Charles Towneley in his Sculpture Gallery

Canvas. 50 × 40 in. Coll: Lord O'Hagan. Exh: R.A., 1790, No. 191. Lit: Lady Victoria Manners and G. C. Williamson, *John Zoffany R.A.*, London 1920, pp. 121–4; S. Sitwell, *Conversation Pieces*, London 1936, repr. Pl. 37. In the eighteenth century Charles Towneley (1737–1805) was one of the principal English collectors of classical antiquities. In 1772 he bought 7 Park Street, Westminster (now Queen Anne's Gate), where he is seen seated on the right in his sculpture gallery. His three friends are Charles Greville, M. D'Hancarville (seated) and Thomas Astle. Zoffany has taken the artistic licence of uniting in one room some of the most important marbles from all over the house. On his death his collection was purchased for the British Museum for £20,000, where it formed the most important group of classical sculptures until the arrival of the Elgin Marbles.
Lent by the Burnley Art Gallery and Museum.

JOHN FLAXMAN, R.A. (1755–1826)

407 Apollo and Marpessa

Marble relief. 18½ × 22 in. Deposited as the artist's Diploma Work in 1800.
Lent by the Royal Academy of Arts.

408 Mirror surmounted by Portrait Group

60¼ × 59½ in. Chimney-piece mirror from the Hunting Room, Clandon Park, c. 1775; the oval pastel group by Daniel Gardner. Carved and gilt frame with classical detail. Lit: C. Hussey, *English Country Houses: Early Georgian*, London 1955, pp. 90, 103, fig. 152.
Lent by the Earl of Onslow.

ARTIST UNKNOWN

409 Robert Adam

Canvas. 50 × 40 in. Coll: sold from the Adam family home, Blair Adam, 1926. Lit: J. Swarbrick, *Robert Adam*, 1915, p. 300 repr.; J. Steegman and C. K. Adams, article on portraits of Adam, *Architectural Review*, March 1942, pp. 77–8. The influence of Robert Adam on the character of interior decoration and furniture is discussed in the Introduction. In this room there are a number of works of art closely connected with him. It was, for example, for William Weddell, whose bust by Nollekens is No. 352, that he designed the

sculpture gallery at Newby Hall, Yorkshire. The superb Moorfields carpet in the centre of the room was made after Adam's design for the Red Drawing-room at Syon House. He also designed the pair of pedestals (No. 384) and the sideboard (No. 386) for the London house of Sir Watkin Williams-Wynn. There is also furniture from Nostell Priory and Harewood House, in both of which Adam designed and decorated some of the principal rooms. Several pieces of furniture from Harewood designed by Adam and made by Chippendale are shown, including the fine rosewood winecooler (No. 390) which belongs to a famous suite.
Lent by the National Portrait Gallery.

410 Moorfields Carpet

417 × 170 in. Designed by Robert Adam, 1769, for the Red Drawing-room, Syon House. Maker's name and date: *Thomas Moore, 1769.* Octagonal and circular paterae in Greek key, anthemion, and guilloche borders; warp of black wool. This carpet, designed to suit its neo-classic surroundings, is "the nearest approach to perfection in contemporary style". Lit: *D.E.F.*, I, pp. 214–15, fig. 17.
Lent by the Duke of Northumberland.

411 Inlaid Table

29 × 49 × 24 in. Attributed to Peter Langlois, *c.* 1765. One of a pair. Top veneered with harewood and inlaid with paterae, guilloche patterning and husks in a variety of coloured woods; legs and frieze fluted. A pair of card tables at Syon House, decorated in a similar style, are also attributed to this maker. See *Georgian Cabinet-Makers*, R. Edwards and M. Jourdain, 3rd Edition, 1955, p. 238, fig. 229.
Lent by Ministry of Works (Audley End).

412 Silver Tea-urn

H. 19½ in. By Thomas Heming, 1772–73. Oval, with draped linen swags; square base; with arms of Lloyd of Bronwydd.
Lent by the National Museum of Wales.

413 Pair of Carved, Gilt and Painted Torchères

H. 82 in., *c.* 1775. Ram-headed tripods with writhing serpents; candelabra forming part of structure. Lit: *D.E.F.*, III, p. 152, fig. 27.
Lent by the Earl of Onslow.

414 Pembroke Table

29 × 40 × 30 in., *c.* 1775. Veneered with satinwood and inlaid in various woods, with paterae, scroll-work and other motifs in neo-classic taste.

Lent by Mrs. David Gubbay.

INDEX OF LENDERS

INDEX OF LENDERS

114

INDEX OF ARTISTS AND CRAFTSMEN

INDEX OF ARTISTS AND CRAFTSMEN

NOTES

NOTES

NOTES

NOTES

NOTES

NOTES

NOTES

NOTES

NOTES

NOTES

NOTES

London
WM. CLOWES & SONS, Ltd.
Printers to the Royal Academy